THE
LOW RISK
CANCER
COOKBOOK

THE
LOW RISK
CANCER
COOKBOOK

QUICK AND TASTY RECIPES FOR HEALTHY LIVING

ANNE LINDSAY

GRUB STREET · LONDON

Published by Grub Street, The Basement, 10 Chivalry Road, London SW11 1HT

First UK impression 1992

Published by arrangement with Macmillan Canada

British Library Cataloguing in Publication Data
Lindsay, Anne
  Low-risk Cancer Cookbook: Quick Tasty
  Recipes for Healthy Living
  I. Title
  641.5

ISBN 0–948817–55–0

Cover photograph by Tim Imrie
Photographs by Fred Bird
Typesetting by Chapterhouse, Formby
Printed and Bound by Biddles Ltd, Guildford, Surrey

CONTENTS

AUTHOR'S ACKNOWLEDGEMENTS

I would like to thank Anne Dolamore and John Davies of Grub Street for their enthusiasm and hard work on the UK edition of this book. I appreciate the involvement of the The World Cancer Research Fund and am pleased that they will receive royalties from the sale of the book.

Many people helped with the original edition and I would like to thank them all. A special thanks to dietitian, friend and co-worker Shannon Graham for her help in testing recipes. Thanks also to Karen Hanley, a Canadian Cancer Society volunteer who gave hours of her time and made the book possible. Many thanks to Dr A. B. Millar, Professor, Faculty of Medicine, University of Toronto; Dr Meera Jain, Nutritionist, University of Toronto; Dr Peter Scholefield, Executive Director, National Cancer Institute of Canada for reviewing the book.

Most of all thanks to my husband, Bob, and my children Jeff, John and Susie for their love, understanding and constant support.

PUBLISHER'S ACKNOWLEDGEMENTS

Grub Street wish to express their thanks to The World Cancer Research Fund for making this UK edition possible, especially Marilyn Gentry, President, for her enthusiastic support, Sheila Ritchie, and Pat Bacon for nutritional advice and all her hard work in converting the recipes to UK measures.

PREFACE

Can you and your family really lower your chances of getting cancer by eating a better diet? The simple answer is YES.

That statement may surprise you. Indeed, many people are unaware just how important a role is played by their food choices in relation to cancer. Yet research studies from around the world continue to show that the foods we eat may be the single most important factor in the cancer process.

According to estimates by prominent researchers, as many as 40 to 60 per cent of all cancers may be linked to our diets. Some scientists estimate that as many as 35 per cent of cancer deaths are diet related. The Health Education Authority has used that same statistic in its own publications.

There is little question, then, that what you eat can and does make a difference in your cancer risk. This is the message that the World Cancer Research Fund is working to present to everyone because these are facts that affect everyone. So does maintaining a healthy weight, getting sufficient exercise, having regular medical check-ups and following guidelines for early detection of cancer.

Cancer is not an inevitable disease. It currently accounts for one out of every four deaths in Great Britain, but that does not have to be the case. You can begin to take charge. You can do things to reduce your cancer risk and dietary change is one simple but important step in that process.

The Low Risk Cancer Cookbook can show you how simple, beginning to eat for better health can be. It can also show you that eating for lower cancer risk and for better health does not mean that food stops being enjoyable. Neither does it mean that you must give up your favourite foods or the pleasure of interesting meals and exciting new recipes.

You'll find in this cookbook healthy recipes that are also easy and delicious. The basis of its approach is not that good health and lower cancer risk can be found only in exotic, strange or expensive foods. Rather, the key here is good nutrition, a balanced diet and an increased awareness of which foods promote good health, and which foods should be eaten in moderation.

The World Cancer Research Fund focuses, in both its research and education programmes, on the role of diet in the cancer process. Researchers now know that certain nutrients within foods can promote cancer and other nutrients can help to inhibit the development of cancer and thus lower cancer risk.

For example, you'll find in this book an increased emphasis on reducing fat in the diet. It is almost universally conceded that doing so is the most positive thing you can do for better health. Current studies say that the average UK citizen gets about 42 per cent of his or her daily calories from dietary fat. That's much too high. According to the World Cancer Research Fund and most other health authorities, dietary fat should contribute 30 per cent or less of daily calories.

You'll find as you read and follow the recipes in *The Low Risk Cancer Cookbook*, that reaching that 30 per cent level is not difficult. Many traditional recipes can easily be revamped to be lower in fat, yet still as delicious as ever. You'll find it's a goal that can be achieved while still enjoying the pleasure of good foods.

You'll also find an increased emphasis here in recipes that use more fruits, vegetables and whole grains. It's an important and essential change to make. Research has linked many of the vitamins and other nutrients in fruits, vegetables and whole grains to lower cancer risk. From beta carotene to vitamin C to increased consumption of fibre, these foods supply nutrients which help the body to defend itself against the cancer risk we face every day. The current recommendation is for each of us to consume at least five servings of fruit and vegetables each day. Many of the tempting recipes in this cookbook make that easy to do.

The Low Risk Cancer Cookbook can help put you on the road to good nutrition and lower cancer risk. Make a start today with some of the delicious dishes you'll find in here and you'll be on the threshold of a healthier life.

Marilyn Gentry
President
World Cancer Research Fund

INTRODUCTION

Whoever would have thought that food could become such a source of fear and suspicion? There seem to be so many conflicting media reports on the effects of certain food choices that one could almost give up all hope of ever finding a truly healthy diet. The result of such misleading stories is that they discourage people from doing anything positive at all.

And there's plenty to be positive about. The really exciting news is the particularly encouraging scientific evidence that some simple and straightforward changes in our diets can benefit our general health, weight, hearts and even reduce our risk of developing cancer.

The World Cancer Research Fund (WCRF) focuses exclusively on the area of diet and cancer. Through both research and public education programmes, the WCRF works to expand the understanding of the link between our food choices and the cancer process. Scientists estimate that at least 35 per cent of all cancers are caused by diet*, a factor in our lives that we can take control of. In fact diet may play an even greater role in cancer rates than smoking does (estimated at 30 per cent).

Percentages of Cancer Deaths Attributable to Various Factors

	Accepted Averages	Actual Range
Food Additives†	1%	−5% to 2%
Pollution	2%	less than 1% to 5%
Alcohol	3%	2% to 4%
Occupation	4%	2% to 40%
Tobacco	30%	25% to 40%
Diet	35%	10% to 70%

†Food additives range from a negative 5% to a positive 2% because it is believed that some may be helpful in reducing cancer risk.
Abridged from Doll and Peto (1981)

Some media reports might lead us to believe that the major cancer culprits in food are the chemical additives in processed foods or even insecticide residues on fruits and vegetables. However, these are, relatively speaking, thought to be insignificant. The real villains are in fact the foods which we choose to eat each day, and the good news is, choice is something over which we *do* have control.

For decades, researchers have detected a link between diet and cancer, but only recently have they begun to uncover the details and importance of that relationship. We now know that certain things we eat, such as fat, may increase our risk of developing certain cancers, especially of the breast and colon. On a positive note, other things such as fibre may help protect us against cancers, particularly those of the stomach and colon.

*Briefing Paper on "Diet & Cancer", HEA Report 1990.

While we are still a long way from prescribing the perfect cancer prevention diet for everyone, we do know enough to recommend simple steps to improve our diets in ways that may reduce cancer risk.

In 1982, the United States' National Institutes of Health concluded that the data linking diet to cancer was convincing enough to justify issuing dietary guidelines on ways to avoid cancer through dietary changes. These changes have been supported by many later reports from all over the world, including the European Community and the World Health Organisation.

The World Cancer Research Fund has drawn on these reports to develop four simple dietary guidelines which could help people lower their risk of developing cancer. The recipes in this book are based on the following guidelines:

Dietary Guidelines to Lower Your Cancer Risk

1. **Cut down the amount of fat in your diet, both saturated and unsaturated, from the current average of approximately 42 per cent to a level of 30 per cent of total calories.**

2. **Eat more fruits, vegetables and whole grain cereals.**

3. **Consume salt-cured, salt-pickled and smoked foods only in moderation.**

4. **Drink alcohol in moderation, if at all.**

A 1991 British Government Green Paper, ''The Health of the Nation'', made dietary recommendations very much in line with the WRCF Dietary Guidelines. The recommendations were based on an earlier report by the Committee on Medical Aspects of Food Policy (COMA). The Health Education's briefing paper, ''Diet and Cancer'', produced jointly with the Department of Health as part of 1989 Europe Against Cancer, comes to many of the same conclusions.

First, the bad news

Fats

Of all the foods we eat, fat appears to contribute most to increased cancer risk. Research data strongly implicates high fat consumption in cancers of the colon, breast and prostate; three of the most common cancers in Britain. Fat contributes about 42 per cent of the calories which the average Briton consumes each day.

In one British study of colorectal (cancers of the colon and rectum) cancer, the highest risk factor was found to be fat intake, with the risk increasing with greater consumption. Men eating more than 100 grams of fat per day were at 70 per cent higher risk than those who ate less than 100 grams of fat per day. Women eating more than 70 grams (about 36 per cent of total calories), were at twice as high a risk as women who ate 70 grams of fat a day.

Breast cancer is also strongly associated with high fat consumption. Research indicates that breast cancer rates are lowest in countries where the fat intake is also low, such as Thailand, Japan and Mexico, and high where intake too is high; Britain, Canada, United States, Denmark and New Zealand.

Scientists believe that fat may in fact play several roles in the cancer process. With some cancers, fat may have an 'initiating' effect; actually causing the genetic changes in cells. In other cancers, it may act as the 'promoter'; furthering the malignant development of changes already initiated.

It is still unclear how fat works in the cancer process. Some evidence indicates that fat seems to affect hormone levels, and since cancers of the reproductive system are influenced by hormones, it is possible that fats and hormonal regulation may act together in the development of cancers of the breast, uterus, ovary and prostate. A theory on bowel cancer suggests that fat's role in the secretion of bile acids and bile steroids in the digestive system may increase the proportion of certain bacteria in the bowel. The result could be the bile acids and bacteria interacting to form carcinogens.

It is important to note that cancer research does not identify one particular kind of fat – saturated or unsaturated – as the promoting agent. All kinds seem to be involved. While saturated fats and cholesterol have been specifically implicated as factors in coronary heart disease, it appears that total fat consumption is the important factor in the cancer process.

Hence, the important message in relation to cancer risk is that we should all be aiming for a diet which is lower in fat. This has been a guiding factor behind most of the recipes in this cookbook and you'll find that many of your favourite foods and recipes can be just as delicious and much more healthy when prepared to be lower in fat.

Obesity

People who are significantly overweight (approximately 40 per cent or more above their ideal weight), appear to have a higher cancer risk; as much as 50 per cent higher in some cancer research studies. It is not clear however, whether it is the extra pounds or types of food eaten which are responsible for this effect.

A 12 year study in the United States indicated that marked obesity was linked to higher death rates from cancers of the gall bladder, kidney, stomach, colon, breast and endometrium (lining of the uterus) when compared with that found in people of normal weight. Other studies have confirmed that being overweight increases the incidence of endometrial and breast cancer in women after menopause. Laboratory research has shown that maintaining a normal body weight can reduce cancer rates and lengthen longevity.

To maintain a desirable body weight, it is important to balance calorie intake with physical activity. The recipes in this WCRF book encourage eating low-calorie, nutrient-rich foods such as fruits, vegetables, grain cereals and pulses. At the same time, they provide delicious alternatives to calorie-laden, high-fat foods.

Alcohol

Drinking alcohol appears to increase the incidence of several forms of cancer. Even moderate alcohol consumption has been linked to greater risks for developing cancers of the breast, rectum and pancreas. Heavy drinkers have a particularly high risk of cancers of the mouth, oesophagus and throat. Heavy beer drinking has been implicated in increased risks of rectal cancer. And in alcohol abusers who have developed cirrhosis of the liver, alcohol thus increases the risk of developing cancer of the liver.

In addition to the direct harm alcohol can cause the body, heavy drinking can also interfere with healthy eating. Alcohol is high in calories as well as containing few (if any) nutrients, and can displace from the diet more wholesome foods containing nutrients which may avert certain types of cancer.

As a general guide, we would recommend that men should limit their intake to no more than two or three units of alcohol a day and women to less than two units of alcohol per day. A unit of alcohol is the equivalent of a half pint of beer or lager, a glass of wine, a single measure of spirit or a small glass of sherry.

Nitrate, salt and smoke

Cured meats, such as bacon, sausages and cold cuts, contain nitrate, a chemical used to prevent botulism. In the digestive system however, nitrites enhance the formation of nitrosamines; cancer-causing agents linked to stomach and oesophageal cancers. Incidence of these cancers is high in countries where people eat a lot of salt-cured and pickled foods (such as Japan and China), or where nitrate and nitrite are common in food and water (as in Columbia).

Nitrates which are converted to nitrite in the body, are found naturally in many foods (including spinach and beetroot), and are not thought to present a problem when eaten in sensible amounts. Some nitrate-containing foods also contain vitamin C, which blocks the conversion of nitrite to nitrosamines.

Salt-cured and salt-pickled foods should be consumed in moderation because of their high salt content. The sodium in salt can also lead to raised blood pressure. Thus food selection is particularly important as about 80 per cent of the salt Britons' consume is in the food they buy, whereas only 20 per cent is added during cooking or at the table. While the impact of salty foods on cancer risk is not entirely clear, high salt intake may be related to stomach cancer.

Smoke ingested from smoked hams, sausages, fish and other meats, contains tars and other substances which may cause cancer.

Grilling food, particularly fatty food, over open flames can also create cancer-causing substances. When fat drips onto a wood or charcoal fire, potent carcinogens form and may be deposited on the food by the smoke or flames. So it is important to avoid eating charred food since the charred material contains high concentrations of carcinogens.

Now the good news

Vitamins

Among the dietary elements that seem to protect against cancer, vitamin A and C seem to be the most important. Several studies of large groups all over the world have shown that foods containing vitamin A may lower the risk of cancers of the larynx, oesophagus, lung and bladder. Scientists believe that vitamin A may be an agent that can reduce the tendency for malignant cells to multiply.

Most of the vitamin A research involves beta-carotene, a compound found in dark green and yellow vegetables and fruits, which converts to vitamin A in the body. Vitamin A itself (preformed retinol), is found in such foods as liver and milk. Both forms of the vitamin appear to provide cancer protection. Unlike beta-carotene however, vitamin A in the form of retinol is toxic when taken in excess of recommended amounts.

Foods containing vitamin C may be helpful against cancers of the oesophagus and stomach. Experiments have shown that vitamin C inhibits the conversion of nitrites found in cured foods to cancer causing nitrosamines in the body.

WCRF and other health organisations strongly discourage people from attempting to meet their needs for vitamins by taking supplements. Pills are not a good substitute for foods, which are very complex mixtures of essential nutrients, some of which may also be important to cancer prevention.

Fibre

Dietary fibre is the part of cereals, fruits and vegetables which is not digested, or is only partially digested. Long considered unnecessary 'roughage', fibre is now recognised for its important contribution to preventing constipation and preventing more serious bowel disorders.

International population studies support an association between high-fibre diets and low incidence of colorectal cancer. In Western countries, where risk of colorectal cancer is high, diets are characteristically low in fibre, whereas the opposite is true in the Third World countries.

While fibre's protective mechanism has not been identified, there are several theories. One is that fibre absorbs water and increases the bulk of waste products, thereby diluting the concentrations of cancer-causing agents in the bowel. Another is that by speeding the movements of foods through the system, fibre reduces the amount of time carcinogens are in contact with the bowel. Fibre may alter bile acids or bacteria in the colon, thus preventing the development of cancer promoting agents.

Health experts recommend an average consumption level of 18 grams of fibre a day with an upper limit to 32 grams (on average, British adults consume only about 12 grams a day). This dietary fibre should come from a variety of fruits, vegetables, whole grain cereals and pulses (such as lentils, beans and peas), rather than from fibre supplements.

Brassica vegetables

One of the surprises in diet/cancer research has been the lowly cabbage. The cabbage and its relatives appear to protect against some cancers of the gastrointestinal tract. Both population studies and laboratory research show that brassica vegetables (such as broccoli, cabbage, sprouts, cauliflower and turnips) may reduce the incidence of cancers of the colon, stomach and oesophagus, as well as being highly effective in inhibiting the effect of cancer causing chemicals.

Additives and other areas of investigation

Although the hazards of food additives make sensational stories in the media, the importance of food additives in the cancer process is thought to be insignificant.

Many other substances are being investigated to determine their role, if any, in cancer. Some of these including selenium, calcium, and vitamin E have shown promise as protectors, but the results are not yet conclusive.

Using the Dietary Guidelines

In the following pages, there are dozens of suggestions and hundreds of recipes to help you plan a healthier style of eating. The underlying message is: Eat a variety of foods in moderation. Cut down on fat and eat more fibre.

1. Cut down the amount of fat in your diet, both saturated and unsaturated, from the current average of approximately 42% to a level of 30% of total calories.

Most of us in Britain have been living a little too literally off the fat of the land: about 42 per cent of the calories we consume are from fat. The World Cancer Research Fund's recommended reduction is thought to be low enough to reduce cancer risk while moderate enough to be realistic.

Cutting down on fat has other benefits. You might lower your blood cholesterol level and consequently your risk of heart disease. Dieters who reduce fat intake and don't make up the calories with other food will lose weight.

We're talking here about cutting down on fat—not cutting out fat. We still need some fat to add flavour and richness to foods. All body tissues contain fat; it is needed for the constant manufacture of new cells. Fatty deposits serve as reserves of energy and protect our vital organs. Fats are also carriers of the fat-soluble vitamins A, D and E.

You can measure fat in terms of both weight (e.g. grams) and energy (e.g. calories). One gram of fat supplies nine calories (one gram of protein or of carbohydrate supplies four calories).

It's not easy to change the habits of a lifetime, but reducing fat intake to 30 per cent of your total calories needn't be an exercise in penance. If you normally eat about 2,000 calories a day, for example, 40 per cent of which is fat (800 calories ÷ 9 = 88 g) the reduction to 30 per cent (600 calories ÷ 9 = 66 g) would mean cutting out only 200 calories, or 22 grams of fat. That amounts to one ounce (25 g) of butter and one tablespoon (15 ml) of mayonnaise. To find out how many grams of fat you should cut in a day, refer to Appendix, page 228.

Since saturated or animal fats are associated with increased risk of heart disease, it makes sense to start there. If you don't have time for complicated calculations, the three easiest ways to reduce fat are:

- Trim fat off meats.
- Use less butter, margarine and oil.
- Eat fewer rich desserts (pastries, whipped cream).

Adjusting your cooking methods is another way to reduce fat intake: steam, poach, roast and bake instead of frying.

And don't underestimate the fat hidden in foods such as baked goods, meat dishes, sauces and desserts. (See Tables C, D and E on pages 230–4 for the fat content of several common foods.)

Much of the fat we eat could be reduced without sacrificing taste. The following are fat-containing foods you might eat in a typical day, with some leaner substitutions. You don't have to make them all every day: just aim to reduce your fat intake.

Cut the Fat

Instead of	Choose	Grams fat saved
Fried egg (8)*	Boiled or poached egg (5)*	3
2 pats of butter on toast (8)	1 pat butter (4)	4
Cream in coffee (3)	semi-skimmed milk in coffee (0)	3
Hamburger, $\frac{1}{4}$ lb (20)	Tuna sandwich (12)	8
Salad with French dressing (6)	Salad with diet dressing (2)	4
Ice cream (8)	Low-fat yogurt (2)	6
8 oz/250 g sirloin steak (20)	4 oz/125 g sirloin steak (10)	10
Asparagus with Hollandaise sauce (18)	Asparagus with grated mozzarella cheese (6)	12
15 French-fries (12)	Baked potato with 1 pat butter (4)	8
Apple pie (16)	Apple (0)	16
Tea with cream (3)	Tea with semi-skimmed milk (0)	3
2 oz/60 g potato crisps (1 small bag) (24)	24 fl oz/750 ml unbuttered popcorn (2)	22
Danish pastry (19)	Fruit scone (5)	14
	Total grams fat saved	113

*grams fat

2. Eat more fruit, vegetables and whole grain cereals.

British diets tend to be woefully low in fibre, and this guideline can help make an improvement. It's not enough to switch to wholewheat bread, though this is a good start. Nutritionists say that for general health we should have 18 grams of fibre per day. Even rich sources of fibre have only about five grams per serving, so that means eating several servings a day. It's wise to work up to the desired level gradually: digestive systems not used to much fibre may object to a sudden influx of it.

The following table lists excellent and good sources of fibre. Aim for three to five servings from the Excellent list or seven from the Good list (you can mix and match, of course). The ratings assume you eat the edible skins of fruits and vegetables.

CHOOSE SEVERAL FIBRE-CONTAINING FOODS EACH DAY

Excellent Sources (4 g or more/serving)	Good Sources (2 to 3.9 g/serving)
BREAD AND CEREALS	
All-Bran	Bran Flakes
Shredded wheat (2 biscuits)	Shreddies
	Muesli
	Fruit 'n' Fibre
	Sultana Bran
	Weetabix
	Wholemeal Bread (1 slice)
	Wholemeal Roll
VEGETABLES	
Beans, baked, tinned	Sweetcorn
Beans, broad, red kidney, soaked and boiled	Peas, green
	Spinach
Chick Peas, soaked and boiled	Sweet potato
Potato, baked with skin	Lentils, boiled
	Potato, boiled
	Parsnips
	Brussels sprouts
	Beans, green
FRUITS	
	Apricots, dried
	Figs, dried
	Prunes, dried
	Dates
	Apple, raw with skin
	Pear, raw with skin
	Orange
	Raspberries

Although nuts are a good source of fibre, they are also high in fat, and it is for this reason The World Cancer Research Fund recommends that you eat only small quantities of both nuts and avocados.

Some people worry that they will be uncomfortable or have gas if they increase their fibre intake. Such problems can be easily overcome by changing your diet gradually, over the course of a week or so, and ensuring that you drink enough liquids every day—3–5 pts/2 to 3 litres of water, milk, juices, tea, coffee and other beverages are recommended.

Some foods that seem to be likely candidates for high-fibre status are in fact poor sources: brown rice, corn-flake cereals, lettuce, green peppers and grapes are some examples.
Add extra fibre to your diet with:
- lentils in meat loaf
- wholewheat tea-cake
- oatmeal toppings on fruit crisps
- lentils or legumes in soups
- legumes in salads (chick peas, kidney beans)
- fresh fruit for breakfast instead of juice

Your mother was right when she told you to eat your vegetables: they are among the few foods that can be unreservedly recommended. Fruits are another. With their enormous variety, fruits and vegetables can offer not only fibre and vitamins A and C, but almost every other essential nutrient, and most of them are fat and calorie bargains, too. You should have four or five servings of fruits and vegetables each day, at least two of them vegetables. Dark green and deep yellow vegetables and fruits are rich sources of vitamin A (in the form of carotene), so choose them often.

Eat Your Greens—and Yellows

Excellent sources of carotene	Good sources of carotene
broccoli	apricots
cantaloupe melon	beetroot greens
carrots	nectarines
spinach	peaches
pumpkin	plums
sweet potatoes	tomatoes
	watermelon

See also lists of excellent vitamins A and C recipes, pages 238, 239.

The vitamin C group is another category of fruits and vegetables that seems to play a role in cancer prevention. Everyone knows that citrus fruits (oranges, grapefruit, lemons, limes) are high in vitamin C, but remember, when you select fruit juices such as apple, grape or pineapple, or fruit drinks, to look for the statement "vitamin C added." Several vegetables are also rich sources of vitamin C. Because vitamin C isn't stored in the body, it's important to include vitamin C-rich foods in your daily menu.

Vitamin C—More Than Just Citrus

Excellent sources	Good sources
apple juice (vitaminized)	cabbage
broccoli	cauliflower
Brussels sprouts	potatoes (baked or steamed)
citrus fruits and juices	swede
green and red peppers	tomatoes and tomato juice
strawberries	

CAUTION: Vitamin C is perishable. Heat, light or exposure to air can destroy it, and it dissolves in cooking water. To preserve it:
- Cover and refrigerate juices after opening.
- Prepare foods just before cooking.
- Cook vegetables with their skins on.
- Steam or bake (don't boil) fruits and vegetables.
- Keep cooking times as short as possible.
- Eat fruits and vegetables raw as often as possible.

And finally, the brassica vegetables. Not only are they packed with vitamins and minerals, but they seem to have an extra protective effect against cancer risk. Have several servings of these vegetables each week.

Cabbages Are Kings

broccoli	kohlrabi
Brussels sprouts	swede
cabbage	turnips
cauliflower	

Since being significantly overweight (approximately 40 per cent above ideal) seems to increase cancer risk, it is important to keep your weight as close as possible to ideal. Maintaining normal weight will also benefit your general health and decrease your risk of other serious diseases, such as heart disease and diabetes.

The best way to lose weight (you've heard it before, but it's still true) is to eat less and exercise more. It is the safest method (no dangerous starvation diets), the one most likely to be permanent (no drastic changes you won't be able to keep up), and it has extra benefits (tones muscles, reduced stress). Other points to remember:

- Lose weight slowly, about two pounds/1kg a week. Anything more puts you in danger of losing essential lean tissue, such as muscle. Depending on physical condition and level of activity, most people can achieve the desired weight loss with about 1,200 calories per day.
- Eat smaller portions.
- Eat less fat. Fat is concentrated calories: one gram of fat has more than twice as many calories as one gram of protein or carbohydrates, so reducing fat intake is the quickest way to cut down on calories. Some fat is essential for nutrition though, so don't try to eliminate it completely. (See pages 10–11 for fat-cutting suggestions.)
- Cut out or cut down on alcohol. Alcohol is the second most concentrated source of calories (see page 11) and is associated with increased cancer risk. As well as being high in calories, the nutritional benefits of alcohol are negligible.
- Avoid foods that are high in sugar.

		Choose to Lose	
Instead of	**Calories**	*Choose*	**Calories**
Doughnut	250	Plain Tea Cake	170
Peanuts, roasted (1 oz/28 g)	170	Twiglets (1 oz/28 g)	110
Chicken, breaded, fried (3 oz/90 g)	220	Roast chicken, light meat only (3 oz/90 g)	150
Mayonnaise (1 tbsp/33 g)	230	low-calorie salad dressing (1 tbsp/33 g)	65
Ice Cream, (1 scoop)	110	Diet Yogurt (1 tub)	75
Chocolate bar (2 oz/56 g)	295	Chocolate Digestive Biscuit	75
Beef, lean and fat (4 oz/125 g)	320	Roast Beef, lean (4 oz/125 g)	220
Spare ribs (4 oz/125 g)	450	Roast Pork, lean (4 oz/125 g)	210
Whole milk (8 fl oz/250 ml)	160	Skimmed milk (8 fl oz/250 ml)	80
Gateau with cream (1 slice)	290	Scone, fruit	150

NB All calorie values are approximate.

3. Consume salt-cured, salt-pickled and smoked foods only in moderation.

Since smoked hams and fish, sausages and other cured foods seem to be associated with cancer risk, it's wise to avoid them as much as possible. Even if it is later found that adequate intake of vitamin C reduces the risk, cured foods are high in fat and salt, which are linked to cancer and hypertension.

4. Drink alcohol in moderation, if at all.

Given the substantial amount of evidence indicating a relationship between alcohol and cancer, it is advisable to consider the wide range of alternatives available. Besides limiting the amount you drink, a few good tips are to eat before you drink, water down your drinks with refreshing mixers or soda, and never drink alcohol to quench your thirst.

Menu Planning

All recipes in this book have been chosen on the basis not only of good taste but of good nutrition. They are high in fibre, low (or lower than usual) in fat, and rich in vitamins and minerals, and they emphasize fruits and vegetables, whole-grain products, and the lean kinds and cuts of meat and fish. Sugar and salt have been kept to a minimum. Some of the recipes are classic favourites, which you will recognize, adapted to reflect the goals of the World Cancer Research Fund.

Use the recipes for everyday meals or for entertaining. Suggested menus are included throughout the book and are listed in the index.

To help you plan your own menus, each recipe gives you the number of calories and grams of fat per serving, as well as fibre, vitamin and mineral ratings. Remember the daily requirements.

- 18 g (range 12–24 g) of fibre, although eating a little more is not harmful, excessive amounts are not recommended.
- fat intake not to exceed 30 per cent of total calories. (To calculate your fat allowance in grams, refer to Appendix, page 228.)

All recipes in this book were analyzed and tested using semi-skimmed milk, low-fat yogurt and low-fat cottage cheese.

Try to include foods from each of the following groups at every meal to ensure a healthy diet. The four food groups and recommended daily servings are:

1. Fruits and vegetables (including green and deep yellow vegetables): 4 or 5 servings (serving size 3–4 oz/100 g)

2. Breads and cereals (including pasta, rice): 3 to 5 servings (serving size: 1 slice bread, or roll; 1 oz/25 g breakfast cereal, 5–6 oz/150 g cooked rice, 8 oz/225 g pasta)

3. Milk and milk products (including cheese, yogurt): 2 to 4 servings (serving size: 8 fl oz/250 ml milk, yogurt or cottage cheese; 1½ oz/45 g Cheddar cheese)

4. Meat, fish, poultry and alternatives (such as peanut butter, beans, lentils, cheese, eggs): 2 servings (serving size: 2 to 3 oz/60 to 90 g cooked lean meat, fish or poultry; 4 tbsp/60 ml peanut butter; 8 fl oz/250 ml cooked dried peas, beans or lentils; 1½ oz/45 g Cheddar or cottage cheese; 2 eggs). 3 oz/90g of cooked meat means a piece of sirloin steak about 4 × 2 × ½ inches/10 × 5 × 1 cm.

Liquids: A daily intake of 3–5 pts/2 to 3 litres of liquid (including soups, juices and beverages) is recommended.

To see if you need to adjust your eating habits, keep track of your diet for several days. Work out the amount of fat and fibre you are eating, and whether you are eating enough of the foods above. You can then make changes to your diet accordingly.

Once you are familiar with which foods are high in fat and fibre and which are low, you can plan your menus with this in mind. For example, if you have a meal with a rich dessert, compensate by choosing other foods low in fat for the rest of the menu: use low-fat salad dressing and roast chicken instead of a creamy dressing and fried steak. If you aren't getting enough fibre, add fresh fruit or raw vegetable to your diet.

Once you get used to your new way of eating, you will be able to estimate how you are doing without a lot of calculating.

Comparing Menus

Instead of	Choose
Breakfast	
orange juice	whole orange (more fibre)
Fried egg, tomato and mushroom	Poached egg, grilled tomato and mushroom
croissant with jam and 1 pat butter or margarine	wholewheat toast and jam
coffee with cream	milk, or coffee with semi-skimmed milk
Fast-Food Lunch	
hot dog	slice of cheese pizza
chips	vegetable salad, no dressing
milk shake	semi-skimmed milk
Dinner	
roast pork and gravy	lean pork tenderloin with meat juices
fried potatoes	baked potato with low-fat yogurt and chives
carrots	carrots
lettuce salad with creamy dressing	spinach salad with low-calorie dressing
	wholewheat roll
lemon meringue pie	lemon sorbet
3 glasses wine	1 glass wine spritzer
coffee with cream	coffee with semi-skimmed milk

These menus are relatively low in calories. To suit calorie needs, serve larger portions and add milk, breads or snacks. It is simple to see how you can build your own menu.

	Grams Fibre/ Serving	Grams Fat/ Serving	Calories	% Calories from Fat
① **Everyday Family Meals**				
Breakfast Grapefruit (½) 8 oz	0.2	tr.	24	
Swiss Fruit Muesli (page 226)	5.6	6	282	
Milk (skimmed, 8 fl oz/250 ml)	0	tr.	80	
Lunch Toasted cheese sandwich (with reduced fat cheese) (1½ oz/45 g) with whole-wheat bread (2 slices)	5.2	7.8	311	
Carrot sticks (1 carrot) 6 oz	1.4	0.2	21	
Peaches, tinned in natural juices (¼ tin)	0.8	tr.	39	
Cinnamon Coffee Cake (page 214)	0.7	3.8	172	
Dinner Chicken Dijon (page 88)	0	3.9	190	
Brown rice (1 serving) 150 g	1.2	1.7	212	
Steamed asparagus (1 serving) (5 spears/125 g)	1.8	1	33	
Wholewheat roll	2.6	0.5	97	
Butter (1 tsp/5 g)	0	4	37	
Rhubarb Crumb Pie (page 216)	2.1	3.6	234	
Milk (skimmed, 8 fl oz/250 ml)	0	tr.	80	
Totals with skimmed milk	21.6 g	31.5 g	1812	16%
Totals with semi-skimmed milk	21.6 g	38.5 g	1892	18%
Totals with whole milk	21.6 g	63.5g	1912	30%

tr. = trace

② Everyday Family Meals

		Grams Fibre/ Serving	Grams Fat/ Serving	Calories	% Calories from Fat
Breakfast	Orange (1) 160 g	2.7	0.2	59	
	Breakfast Bran-and-Fruit (pages 222–3) (includes 4 fl oz/125 ml skimmed milk)	6.0	5.1	203	
	with fresh banana 100 g	1.1	0.3	95	
	Slice whole-wheat toast (1)	2.6	0.5	97	
	Jam or marmalade (1 tsp/5 g)	0	0	13	
Lunch	Tri-Colour Bean Soup (page 51)	4.6	1.6	120	
	Whole-Wheat Irish Soda Bread (page 181) with 1 tsp/5 g butter or polyunsaturated margarine	2.9	5.7	180	
	Yogurt (diet) (4 fl oz/125 ml)	0	0.2	75	
	Almond-Apricot Squares (page 184) (2)	4.7	8	154	
Dinner	Marinated Steak (page 102)	0	9	200	
	Mashed Potatoes with Onions (page 170)	2.3	2	123	
	Broccoli and Sweet Pepper Stir-Fry (page 156)	2.5	2	40	
	Poached Pears with Chocolate Sauce (pages 191)	2.0	0.8	168	
	Milk (skimmed, 4 fl oz/125 ml)	0	0	40	
	Totals with skimmed milk	30.8 g	35.4 g	1567	20%
	Totals with semi-skimmed milk	30.8 g	39.1 g	1599	22%
	Totals with whole milk	30.8 g	44.9 g	1650	25%

n.b. Using a low fat spread will provide less fat than butter or margarine.

Everyday Family Meals

	Grams Fibre/ Serving	Grams Fat/ Serving	Calories	% Calories from Fat
Breakfast Orange juice (4 fl oz/125 ml)	tr.	tr.	45	
Branflakes with sultanas (½ oz/15 g)	4.2	0.7	177	
Milk, (Skimmed 8 fl oz/250 ml)	0	tr.	80	
Lunch Bermuda Bean Salad (pages 78–9)	4.5	4	248	
Whole-Wheat Raisin Scone (page 182) (1)	2.9	8	220	
Prune Cake with Lemon Icing (page 199)	2.1	1.3	182	
Milk, (Skimmed 8 fl oz/250 ml)	0	tr.	80	
Banana (1) 100 g	1.1	0.3	95	
Dinner Sole Fillets with Lemon and Parsley (page 119)	0	5.8	138	
Brown rice	1.2	1.7	212	
Steamed green beans 90g	3.7	tr.	23	
Green Salad with Creamy Herb Dressing* (page 82)	0.9	1.6	73	
Chocolate cake 65 g	0.6	7.3	219	
Totals with skimmed milk	21.2 g	30.7 g	1792	15%
Totals with semi-skimmed milk	21.2 g	38.7 g	1858	19%
Totals with whole milk	21.2 g	50.4 g	1962	23%

*These figures are for the large main-course-size serving of salad; the smaller side-salad size has 4 grams of fat and 83 calories.

Everyday Family Meals

	Grams Fibre/ Serving	Grams Fat/ Serving	Calories	% Calories from Fat
Breakfast Stewed prunes (3) 25 g	0.6	0	20	
Weetabix (1)	3.6	1.0	132	
Boiled egg (1)	0	5	74	
Slice whole-wheat toast (1)	2.6	0.5	97	
Butter or polyunsaturated margarine (1 tsp/5 g)	0	4	37	
Milk, (Skimmed, 8 fl oz/250 ml)	0	tr.	80	
Lunch Chicken sandwich with whole-wheat (2) with lettuce or bean sprouts and mayonnaise (1 tsp/5 ml) 2 oz	5.5	7.3	320	
Celery stick (1) 30 g	0.3	tr.	2	
Tangerine (1) 70 g	0.9	tr.	25	
Wheat Germ Crispy Cookies (page 186) (2)	1.8	6	114	
Milk (Skimmed, 8 fl oz/250 ml)	0	tr.	80	
Dinner Old-Fashioned Meat Loaf (page 105)	0.3	9.5	186	
Baked potato (1 med.) 180 g	4.9	0.4	245	
Steamed Brussels sprouts (1 serving 90 g)	2.8	1.2	32	
Lemon Ginger Carrots (page 155) (4 fl oz/125 ml)	2.4	4	69	
Apricot Clafouti (page 210)	1.6	4.4	162	
Totals with skimmed milk	27.3 g	43.4 g	1675	23%
Totals with semi-skimmed milk	27.3 g	50.9 g	1740	26%
Totals with whole milk	27.3 g	62.4 g	1840	31%

Eating Out

There's no reason to throw away your diet resolutions when you eat out or travel. The World Cancer Research Fund's guidelines are flexible enough to accommodate almost any dining situation. Superhuman willpower is not required, only knowledge and foresight—and a little ingenuity.

- Beware of high-fat foods: don't order a succession of rich dishes. Concentrate more on fruits, vegetables and whole-grain foods.
- If you over-indulge on a special occasion, eat moderately for the rest of the day and for a few days after.
- Many restaurants now offer low-calorie or light meals—some even specialize in creating exciting gourmet versions.
- Ask to have a fried dish steamed or grilled; ask for salads with the dressing separate so you can serve yourself; ask to have meats served minus rich sauces or gravy. Many restaurants are becoming accustomed to such requests.
- Split a dish, or several dishes, with your dining companion; many restaurants will serve the two half-portions on separate plates.
- Choose a couple of appetizers instead of an entrée, or order soup and a salad.
- Choose clear instead of cream soups.
- Butter bread or rolls sparingly, or not at all.
- Choose fish or chicken dishes, and avoid those with cream sauces.
- Cut all the fat off meats.
- Avoid sautéed and deep-fried foods.
- If choosing a high-fat food, ask for a small portion.

Breakfasts

Choose:
- fresh fruits and juices
- whole-grain breads and cereals
- poached or boiled eggs (if concerned about cholesterol, limit to 3 per week)
- yogurt with fresh fruit
- low-fat milk instead of cream or whole milk with cereals and coffee or tea

Avoid:
- Danish pastries or croissants
- bacon, sausages, ham
- too much butter or margarine

Lunches and Dinners

Choose:
- pretzels rather than peanuts
- salads—add the dressing yourself or ask for a wedge of lemon. Choose from the salad bar: include spinach, sweetcorn, kidney beans, chick peas
- cottage cheese
- clear soups

- pasta dishes with tomato-based or wine-based sauces rather than sauces made with cream, oil or butter
- chicken or fish dishes, grilled or poached (light sauce only)
- fresh fruit desserts, sorbets and sherbets

Avoid, or choose occasionally and in moderate amounts:
- alcoholic drinks (other possibilities are tomato juice, soda or mineral water)
- quiches (pastry is high in fat)
- pâtés and avocados (high in fat)
- chips
- butter or sour cream on baked potatoes (ask for yogurt and chives or spring onions)
- fatty cuts of beef, pork and lamb (especially in large servings), duck and goose
- high-fat cheeses (Cheddar, cream cheeses)
- barbecued foods
- breaded foods (they're usually fried)
- peanuts and potato crisps (substitute raw vegetables)
- smoked and heavily salted foods: ham, salami, herring
- chocolates
- mousses and rich desserts (chocolate, cream)

Cooking Methods

Cooking methods to avoid or use with caution:
Some cooking methods, such as barbecuing, grilling or smoking, may be harmful. To barbecue safely, wrap food in foil or place it high above the coals and cook slowly. It has been suggested that chemicals that are possibly cancer-causing may form when food is charred. For this reason, and because of the added fat, avoid frying, especially at high temperatures.

Cooking methods to choose:
Baking, roasting (use rack), grilling (don't burn or char), microwave cooking, boiling, steaming (see pages 131 and 162), poaching, stewing and stir-frying (see pages 95–6) are good methods. They require little or no additional fat.

Cooking equipment you need:
- steamer: either the double-boiler type or a basket
- heavy nonstick pan or wok

To preserve vitamins in cooking:
Some vitamins are destroyed by heat; others dissolve in the cooking water. To preserve them as much as possible:
- Cook vegetables quickly just until tender-crisp.
- Use as little water as possible and have it boiling before adding vegetables.
- Use any leftover cooking liquid in soups or stews.
- Use cooking methods that require very little or no liquid at all: microwaving, baking, steaming, foil-wrapped in oven and stir-frying using a small amount of oil.

To reduce fat in cooking:

- Many recipes begin by sautéing vegetables such as onions in butter. In most cases you can reduce the butter at least by half, often to one teaspoon/5 ml; add a few tablespoons/25 ml of white wine or water and cook the vegetables slowly over low heat. This method brings out the flavour just as effectively as the traditional method.
- If oil, margarine or butter is needed for flavour, add it at the end just before serving; you will get the most flavour for the least amount of fat.
- It is very important to use heavy pans, nonstick where possible. This is one of the best ways to cut down on fat without having foods burn or stick.
- Cut off all visible fat before cooking and drain off fat during cooking; make stews or soups using meats or stocks a day in advance and refrigerate overnight—fat solidifies on top and can be easily lifted off.
- Instead of butter or oil for flavour, use herbs and spices, onions or garlic, ginger, lemon juice, mustard.
- Buy the best-quality vegetables in season: they will have the best natural flavour and won't need as much butter or salt.
- Use vegetable purées (coulis) as a sauce rather than butter-based sauces.
- Use a rack in the roasting pan so that the meat doesn't sit in fat.
- Remove the skin from fowl before cooking or eating.
- Choose lean cuts of meat, such as rump steak or sirloin. Avoid prime rib and pork loin.
- Serve 4oz/125 gram portions, or less, of meats; you can extend them and make them more interesting by cooking them with vegetables in stews, soups and stir-fries or with pasta.
- Cut meats into thin slices; it will look like more.
- Reduce oil in standard marinades, or omit oil altogether (see Marinated Leg of Lamb with Coriander, pages 114–15; Marinated Steak, page 102).
- Use skimmed or semi-skimmed milk instead of whole, yogurt instead of sour cream, wine instead of butter or oil.
- Avoid desserts made with double cream; choose desserts based on milk or yogurt.
- Avoid dessert pastries, choose crumbles instead (e.g. instead of double-crust apple pie, choose apple crumble).
- If you're making cakes or other rich desserts, compare various recipes for fat or oil content and choose the one with the lowest amount.
- Use dessert recipes calling for cocoa rather than chocolate, as long as the cocoa recipe doesn't have additional fat.

Shopping

Check the labels on tins and and other containers; they often give the fat and fibre content in grams per serving, plus other nutritional information. When the ingredients are given on a label, they are listed in order of amounts by weight, beginning with the largest amount. Sugars are often listed by kind (invert sugar, glucose, sucrose) and it may be difficult to determine the total amount of sugar.

Choose:
- calorie-reduced or low-fat soups and salad dressings
- low-fat yogurt, milk, ice cream and cheese (see Tables D and E, pages 233 and 234)
- low-fat butter or margarines for spreading (use regular hard margarines or butter for baking)
- lean types and cuts of meat (see Table C, pages 230–2)
- angel cakes; gingersnaps, arrowroot
- turkey that hasn't been injected with fat, i.e., not self-basting
- dark green lettuces or spinach (not iceberg lettuce)
- wholewheat or stone-ground breads, pitta bread, wholewheat crackers, tea-cakes and scones, pasta
- whole-grain cereals, cereals with bran or high fibre (see Table F, pages 235–6)
- fresh fruits and vegetables

Avoid
- processed meats: hot dogs, salami (if purchasing, choose fat-reduced kinds)
- high-fat meats and poultry: duck, goose, minced meat (unless lean), sausages, spare ribs (see Table C, pages 230–2)
- side bacon (very occasionally choose lean ham or back bacon)
- breaded and fried frozen meats and fish, e.g. fish fingers
- tuna fish packed in oil (instead choose tuna packed in brine)
- avocados
- doughnuts, Danish pastries, croissants, pies, pastries, cakes, biscuits
- cereals with sugar and low fibre
- chocolates
- peanuts, potato crisps (choose a low-fat variety if you do buy)

APPETIZERS

Scrumptious snacks and cocktail party titbits are irresistible and first courses are often the most innovative and interesting part of a meal. What's more, they can add valuable nutrients to your diet. But beware, they can also be nutritional hazards.

Pâtés, peanuts, potato crisps, savoury-filled pastries and mayonnaise-based dips are high in fat and should be avoided. Instead, choose crudités (raw vegetables, higher in fibre and vitamins) with a yogurt or cottage cheese-based dip, or savouries with a bread casing (lower in fat than pastry cases). Appetizers such as Prawns Wrapped with Mangetout or Teriyaki Beef Rumaki will be favourites with any crowd and are also low in fat. The recipes in this section of the book will help you plan menus for entertaining that are low in fat and in calories.

Appetizer courses in restaurants can be wonderfully appealing and nutritious. Because some restaurant entrées are very large, appetizers are often just the right size to substitute for a main course.

PRAWNS WRAPPED WITH MANGETOUT

This colourful, delicious hors d'oeuvre is very easy to prepare. Serve any remaining mangetout with a dip or spread, or split them down the centre and fill with cottage cheese. This dish is unusually low in fat and calories.

2 pts	water	1 L
1	thick slice of onion	1
1	garlic clove, halved	1
1	bay leaf	1
2	stalks celery with leaves	2
1 lb	large raw prawns in shells (about 18)	450 g
4 oz	mangetout	125 g
18	wooden cocktail sticks	18

In large saucepan, combine water, onion, garlic, bay leaf and celery; bring to a boil. Reduce heat and simmer for 5 minutes; add prawns and simmer, uncovered, for 3 to 5 minutes or until prawns turn pink.

Drain immediately and chill under cold water. Remove shell and black intestinal vein from each prawn.

Trim mangetout and blanch in boiling water for 2 minutes or just until they are pliable. Drain and plunge into a bowl of ice water to prevent further cooking and to set colour. Drain.

Wrap a mangetout around each prawn and secure with a cocktail stick. Arrange on serving platter or stick into head of cauliflower. Cover and refrigerate until serving time. Makes about 18 (4 servings).

Calories per piece: 14
Grams fat per piece: 0.1
Fibre: Good
Mangetout are a good source of vitamin A and fibre.

CRAB-STUFFED MINI-PITTAS

Mini-pitta bread rounds provide quick and easy containers for countless fillings. The packaged varieties are available in the bread sections of some supermarkets and speciality shops. Choose the wholewheat ones for more flavour and fibre.

1	pkt (8) wholewheat mini-pittas	1
8 oz	crab meat (canned, fresh or frozen)	225 g
2 tbsp	spring onion, sliced	30 ml
4 fl oz	Parsley Dressing* (page 85)	125 ml
½ tsp	lemon juice	2 ml
	Salt and freshly ground pepper	
	Lettuce	

Cut pitta breads in half. Drain crab meat thoroughly. In bowl, combine crab meat, onion, Parsley Dressing, lemon juice, and salt and pepper to taste; and mix lightly. (Add more Parsley Dressing to taste). Line pitta bread pockets with lettuce. Spoon crab meat mixture into each pitta. Refrigerate until needed. Makes 16.

Calories per piece: 40
Grams fat per piece: 0.5
Fibre: 0.7 g

Variations
- Use pitta rounds with any of the salads in salad section of book.
- Line pitta with alfalfa sprouts or bean sprouts and fill with a spoonful of Hummus (page 32); top with Garlic Dip (page 28).
- Substitute cooked or canned salmon, prawn or tuna (not packed in oil) for crab.
- Line pitta with lettuce and fill with Aubergine Caviar (page 31) or Spinach Dip (page 29).

*Make the full recipe of Parsley Dressing and use the rest of it as a dip—its delicious!

CRAB AND CUCUMBER ROUNDS

Diet Hint: Reducing fat content in hors d'oeuvres
- Instead of pastry cases, use bread cases—see Stuffed Mushroom Croustades (page 26).
- To hold fillings, use hollowed-out cherry tomatoes, canned lychees and cucumber slices.
- Avoid pâtés and mayonnaise-based dressings.

Crisp cucumber slices, instead of pastry or bread, make refreshing low-calorie, low-fat canapé bases.

1	cucumber	1
1	can (6 oz/175 g) crab meat	1
2 tbsp	sour cream	30 ml
2 tbsp	chopped chives or spring onion	30 ml
	Salt and freshly ground pepper	
	Paprika	

Run prongs of fork lengthwise along cucumber to make decorative edge on slices. Cut cucumber into slices $\frac{1}{4}$ inch/5 mm thick.

Drain crab meat thoroughly. Mix with sour cream, chives and salt and pepper to taste. Place small spoonful of crab mixture on each cucumber slice. Sprinkle with paprika. Cover and refrigerate for up to 4 hours. Makes about 36.

Calories per round: 4.3
Grams fat per round: 0.2

Hidden Fat in Foods
We all know that foods such as mayonnaise, whipped cream and Cheddar cheese are high in fat. Here are some other foods that are also deceptively high in fat.

	Grams fat/serving
Roasted Peanuts (1 oz/30 g)	15
Potato crisps (1 small bag)	24
Corn chips (1 small bag)	20
Half an avocado	19
Peanut butter (2 tbsp/30 ml)	16
Olives, black (6 medium)	14
Pâté de foie gras (2 tbsp/30 ml)	13
Ice-cream bar, chocolate-coated (2 oz/56 g)	10
Chocolate bar (1 oz/28 g)	9
French-fried potatoes (10 pieces)	7
Boiled or baked potato	trace
Olives, green (8 medium)	6
Egg yolk	5

Opposite:
Teriyaki Beef Rumaki (page 27) Stuffed Mushroom Croustades (page 26) Cherry Tomatoes Stuffed with Spinach Dip (page 29) Prawns Wrapped with Mangetout (pages 22–23) Crab-Stuffed Mini-Pittas (page 23)

GREEN BEAN CRUNCH

Spinach-Stuffed Mushrooms

Fresh white mushrooms are delicious raw. Remove their stems and they're easy to stuff. If you're having a party, make the full recipe of Spinach Dip (page 29) or Parsley Dressing (page 85); use 8 fl oz/250 ml as a stuffing for ½ lb/250 g mushrooms or cherry tomatoes, and the rest as a dip. They're a low-fat, low-calorie appetizer.

Stuffed Cherry Tomatoes

Cherry tomatoes are a colourful fresh-tasting addition to an hors d'oeuvres platter. To stuff, cut off the top of each tomato, hollow out some of the pulp and fill with Hummus (page 32), Spinach Dip (page 29), or Creamy Fresh Dill Dip (page 30).

Cherry tomatoes are a good source of vitamins A and C and are low in fat.

For a salty, crunchy snack that's low in fat and calories, try Green Bean Crunch instead of peanuts or potato crisps. It will be appreciated by dieters who crave salty foods. You can add other raw vegetables such as carrot, kohlrabi, fennel and turnip.

1½ lb	green beans	675 g
½	small head cauliflower	½
8 fl oz	water	250 ml
1	onion, chopped	1
1	large garlic clove, peeled	1
1 tbsp	lemon juice	15 ml
4 tbsp	soy sauce, low-sodium	60 ml
4 tbsp	water	60 ml
1 tbsp	sunflower oil	15 ml
1 tbsp	sesame seeds	15 ml
8	large lettuce leaves	8

Remove stem end of green beans. Cut cauliflower into small florets. In large saucepan, bring 8 fl oz/250 ml water to a boil; add onion, garlic, lemon juice, beans and cauliflower. Reduce heat, cover and simmer until vegetables are tender-crisp, about 8 minutes; drain, and discard garlic. Combine soy sauce, 4 tbsp/60 ml water and oil; pour over vegetables. Cover and refrigerate for at least 1 hour.

Place sesame seeds on baking tray and toast in 325°F/160°C/Gas Mark 3 oven for 5 minutes or until golden brown.

Just before serving, toss vegetable mixture; remove from marinade. Arrange lettuce leaf on each plate. Spoon vegetable mixture onto lettuce and sprinkle with sesame seeds. Makes 8 servings.

Calories per serving: 45
Grams fat per serving: 1.7
Fibre: Good
Vitamin A: Good
Cauliflower is a good source of fibre and of vitamin C.

Opposite:
Balkan Beetroot Cream Soup (pages 36–37)

STUFFED MUSHROOM CROUSTADES

These mushroom appetizers are so delicious, they just melt in your mouth. I first tasted them at caterer Alison Cummings' home. To keep the fat as low as possible, I reduce the butter and use low-fat cheese. You can also use the croustade cases for other savoury fillings—they're much lower in fat and calories than pastry.

24	thin slices bread	24
24	medium white mushrooms	24
Stuffing		
3 oz	fine fresh wholewheat bread crumbs	75 g
1	large garlic clove, chopped	1
4 tbsp	finely chopped fresh parsley	60 ml
	Salt and freshly ground pepper	
$\frac{1}{2}$ oz	butter	15 g
3 oz	grated mozzarella cheese	75 g

Using $2\frac{1}{2}$ inch/6 cm biscuit cutter or glass, cut out 24 rounds of bread. Press bread rounds into a small bun tin. Bake in 300°F/150°C/Gas Mark 2 oven for 20 to 25 minutes or until light brown. Remove from oven and let cool. (Croustades may be prepared in advance and stored in covered container for about 1 week or frozen for longer storage.)

Wash mushrooms and dry with paper towels; remove stems (save for use in soups). Store mushrooms in refrigerator until needed.

Stuffing: In food processor or mixing bowl, combine bread crumbs, garlic, parsley, and salt and pepper to taste; process until combined. Add butter and process just until mixed. (If mixing by hand, use soft or melted butter.) Spoon some stuffing into each mushroom cap; top with grated cheese.

Just before serving, place a mushroom into each bread case. Place on baking sheet and bake in 400°F/200°C/Gas Mark 6 oven for 10 minutes or until hot. If desired, grill for last minute. Serve hot. Makes 36.

Calories per piece: 53
Grams fat per piece: 1
Fibre: Two pieces are a good source of fibre.

TERIYAKI BEEF RUMAKI

Cocktail Party for 25
Plan on 6 to 8 pieces per
person. Multiply recipes
according to number of guests.
Teriyaki Beef Rumaki
(page 27)
Crab-Stuffed Mini-Pittas
(page 23)
Parsley or Watercress Dressing
with raw vegetables (page 85)
Mushrooms stuffed with
Spinach Dip (page 29)
Prawns Wrapped with
Mangetout (pages 22–3)
Salmon Mousse with Dill
(page 33)

*Use naturally brewed light or
sodium-reduced soy sauce for
lower sodium (salt) content.

Wrap tender strips of marinated beef around crunchy water
chestnuts for a delectable hot appetizer.

12 oz	sirloin, or topside or other lean steak (about $\frac{1}{2}$ inch/1 cm thick)	350 g
4 tbsp	soy sauce*	60 ml
1	garlic clove, chopped	1
1 tbsp	onion, finely diced	15 ml
1 tbsp	granulated sugar	15 ml
1 tsp	Worcestershire sauce	5 ml
$\frac{1}{2}$ tsp	ground ginger	2 ml
1	can (10 oz/284 ml) water chestnuts	1
	wooden cocktail sticks	

Place meat in freezer for about 30 minutes or until firm
for easier slicing. Cut off any fat. Slice meat across the grain
into very thin strips about $\frac{1}{8}$ inch/3 mm thick and
3 inches/8 cm long.

In a bowl combine soy sauce, garlic, onion, sugar,
Worcestershire sauce and ginger. Add meat and stir to coat
strips evenly. Marinate for 30 minutes at room temperature,
stirring occasionally, or overnight in refrigerator.

Drain meat. Wrap one strip around each water chestnut
and secure with cocktail stick. Arrange on baking sheet or in
shallow glass serving dish. Grill for 3 to 4 minutes or until
piping hot and cooked medium-rare (or microwave on High
for 3 to 4 minutes, rotating dish $\frac{1}{4}$ turn halfway through
cooking time). Makes about 25.

Calories per piece: 37
Grams fat per piece: 0.8
Four pieces of rumaki are a good source of iron.

GARLIC DIP

Serve as a dip with raw vegetables, or as a sauce over baked potatoes, sliced tomatoes or cucumber, steamed green beans or fish fillets.

<table>
<tr><td>12 oz</td><td>plain yogurt</td><td>350 ml</td></tr>
<tr><td>4 tbsp</td><td>chopped spring onions or chives</td><td>60 ml</td></tr>
<tr><td>2</td><td>garlic cloves, chopped</td><td>2</td></tr>
<tr><td>1 tbsp</td><td>vegetable oil</td><td>15 ml</td></tr>
<tr><td>½ tsp</td><td>granulated sugar</td><td>2 ml</td></tr>
</table>

	plain yogurt	
12 oz	plain yogurt	350 ml
4 tbsp	chopped spring onions or chives	60 ml
2	garlic cloves, chopped	2
1 tbsp	vegetable oil	15 ml
½ tsp	granulated sugar	2 ml

In bowl, combine yogurt, onions, garlic, oil and sugar. Mix thoroughly. Cover and refrigerate until needed. Makes about 12 oz/350 ml.

	Per 1 tbsp/15 ml	Per 4 tbsp/60 ml
Calories:	24	96
Grams fat:	2	7

5 tbsp/75 ml dip is a good source of calcium.

Variation
Curry Dip: Add 1 tsp/5 ml each curry powder and cumin to Garlic Dip. Amount of onions and garlic can be reduced.

Diet Hint: Reducing fat content in finger foods, snacks and first courses

Instead of	Choose
Guacamole or mayonnaise	Cottage cheese or yogurt-based dips
Peanuts and potato crisps	Unbuttered popcorn and pretzels
Cream crackers	Wholewheat crackers
Biscuits and cheese	Pitta bread
Oysters Rockefeller	Raw oysters
Caviar	Prawns
Lobster Newburg	Lobster pieces
Cocktail sausages or frankfurters	Lean meats
Meat pâté	Vegetable pâté
Cream soup	Gazpacho or consommé
Pasta with cream sauce	Pasta with tomato sauce
Mayonnaise dressed salads (egg, potato)	Green salads with yogurt dressing
Bloody Mary	Tomato juice

SPINACH DIP

Serve with broccoli, mangetout, asparagus, carrots, turnip, green beans, cauliflower and/or cherry tomatoes for good to excellent fibre.

Perfect for dipping vegetables, this is also delicious as a filling for mushrooms and cherry tomatoes or as a dressing for salads and chilled cooked vegetables. Spinach is an excellent source of fibre and vitamin A (*carotene*).

1	pkg (10 oz/300 g) frozen chopped spinach, or 1 lb/450 g fresh	1
8 fl oz	sour cream	250 ml
4 fl oz	plain yogurt	125 ml
8 tbsp	fresh parsley, chopped	120 ml
4 tbsp	finely chopped spring onions (including tops)	60 ml
1 tsp	salt	5 ml
	Freshly ground pepper	

If using fresh spinach, trim tough ends. Boil or steam spinach until wilted; drain thoroughly and chop. If using frozen, defrost and squeeze by hand to remove all moisture or wrap in paper towels and squeeze.

In bowl, mix together spinach, sour cream, yogurt, parsley, onions, salt, and pepper to taste. Cover and refrigerate for at least 4 hours or overnight to blend flavours. Makes 1 pt/500 ml dip.

	Per 1 tbsp/15 ml
Calories:	17
Grams fat:	1
Vitamin A:	Good
Folacin:	Good

Spinach is an excellent source of fibre and vitamin A.

CRUDITÉS WITH CREAMY FRESH DILL DIP

*If using dried dillweed, add 3 tbsp/45 ml more chopped fresh parsley.

Prepare a colourful selection of raw vegetables—cauliflower, carrots, red, yellow and green peppers, mangetout, baby corn, courgettes, chicory, green beans, celery, fennel; cut them into strips suitable for dipping and arrange on a large platter with dip in centre.

4	carrots	4
2	sweet red, yellow or green peppers	2
$\frac{1}{2}$	small cauliflower	$\frac{1}{2}$
2	chicory	2
4 oz	mushrooms	125 g
Creamy Dill Dip		
4 tbsp	chopped fresh dill (or 2 tsp/10 ml dried dillweed)*	60 ml
2 tbsp	chopped fresh parsley	30 ml
8 oz	cottage cheese	250 ml
3 tbsp	plain yogurt	45 ml
	Salt and freshly ground pepper	

Cut carrots and peppers into strips. Separate cauliflower in florets. Separate chicory leaves. Halve mushrooms if large. Refrigerate until serving time.

Creamy Dill Dip: Chop dill and parsley in food processor; add cottage cheese, yogurt, and salt and pepper to taste. Process with pulse facility or on-off turns to mix. Refrigerate.

At serving time, arrange vegetables on platter. Place dip in centre. Makes 10 servings (10 fl oz/300 ml dip).

Per 1 tbsp/15 ml of dip
Calories: 12
Grams fat: 0.25
Fibre will vary depending on vegetables (see chart, page 236).

Compare	Per 10 fl oz/300 ml	
Dip made with:	Calories	Grams fat
plain low-fat yogurt	143	3.4
low-fat cottage cheese	230	4.4
sour cream	416	40
mayonnaise	1,616	179

AUBERGINE CAVIAR

Often called Poor Man's Caviar, this Mediterranean dip is delicious with raw vegetables or as a spread with melba toast.

1	large aubergine (about 1¼ lb/575 g)	1
3	spring onions, finely chopped	3
1	large garlic clove, chopped	1
1	large tomato, peeled and chopped	1
½	celery stalk, finely chopped	½
4 tbsp	green pepper, finely chopped (optional)	60 ml
1 tbsp	fresh lemon juice	15 ml
2 tsp	vegetable oil	10 ml
½ tsp	salt	2 ml
¼ tsp	freshly ground pepper	1 ml

Prick aubergine in several places with a fork. Place on baking sheet and bake in 400°F/200°C/Gas Mark 6 oven for 45 minutes or until soft, turning once or twice during baking. Let cool, then peel and chop finely.

In mixing bowl, combine aubergine, onions, garlic, tomato, celery and green pepper if using; toss to mix. Add lemon juice, oil, salt and pepper; mix well. Cover and refrigerate for at least 1 hour to blend flavours. Makes 1¼ pts/750 ml.

	Per 1 tbsp/15 ml	4 tbsp/60 ml
Calories:	5.8	23
Grams fat:	0.3	1.2

4 oz cup/125 ml of Aubergine Caviar is a good source of fibre.

Compare	4 tbsp/60 ml	
	Calories	Grams fat
Chicken liver pâté	276	26.4
Aubergine Caviar	23	1.2

HUMMUS (CHICK PEA DIP)

Summer Lunch or Picnic
White wine spritzers
Wholewheat pitta bread filled
with Hummus, topped with
alfalfa sprouts or shredded
lettuce, and sliced tomatoes or
sweet red peppers and a
spoonful of yogurt seasoned
with curry or cumin.
Strawberries

Serve this Middle Eastern classic with pitta bread or
vegetables as an appetizer or for lunch, snacks or a picnic.
For a casual dinner, add vegetable soup to the menu.

4 tbsp	tahini (sesame paste) or peanut butter	60 ml
½ tsp	(approx) cumin or more to taste	2 ml
½ tsp	salt	2 ml
2	large garlic cloves, chopped	2
2 tbsp	lemon juice	30 ml
2 tbsp	hot water	30 ml
1	can (15.2 oz/432 g) chick peas, drained	1
	Chopped fresh parsley (optional)	

In small bowl, combine tahini, cumin, salt and garlic;
while stirring, slowly pour in lemon juice, then hot water.
Purée chick peas in a blender or a food processor, or pass
through a food mill; add tahini mixture to purée and process
or mix well. Taste and add more cumin and salt if desired.
Spread hummus on dinner plate and sprinkle with chopped
parsley. Makes 12 fl oz/375 ml.

	Per 1 tbsp/15 ml	Per 4 tbsp/60 ml
Calories:	38	152
Grams fat:	1.5	6
Fibre: Good—4 tbsp/60 ml: 3.4 g		

SALMON MOUSSE WITH DILL

This smooth and creamy spread looks pretty when unmoulded and surrounded with crackers, melba toast or fresh vegetables. And because it's made without whipping cream and mayonnaise, it's low in fat and calories. Try to use sockeye salmon for its bright red colour.

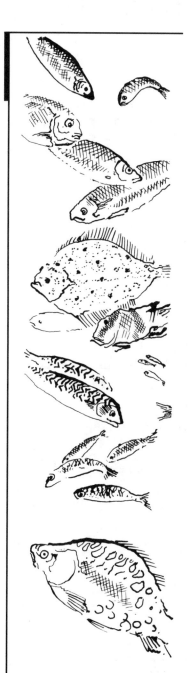

1	envelope unflavoured gelatine	1
4 fl oz	water or clam juice	125 ml
5 tbsp	chopped fresh dill or 1 tsp/5 ml dried dillweed	75 ml
2 tbsp	grated onion	30 ml
1 tbsp	lemon juice	15 ml
1 tsp	salt	5 ml
Dash	Tabasco sauce	Dash
7 oz	plain yogurt	175 ml
5 oz	sour cream	125 ml
1 stick	finely chopped celery	1 stick
2	cans (each 7¾ oz/220 g) sockeye salmon, drained	2

In small saucepan, sprinkle gelatine over cold water; let stand until softened, about 5 minutes. Warm over medium heat until gelatine is dissolved. Let cool to room temperature. Stir in dill, onion, lemon juice, salt, Tabasco, yogurt, sour cream and celery. Refrigerate until mixture begins to set.

Remove skin from salmon (but keep bones—they're an excellent source of calcium); mash salmon with a fork or process in a food processor. Mix into gelatine mixture. Spoon into 2 pt/1 L mould. Cover and refrigerate until firm, at least 3 hours.

Dip the mould into warm water for a few minutes. Unmould onto serving plate. Surround with crackers, melba toast, or fresh vegetables. Makes about 2 pts/1 L.

	Per 1 tbsp/15 ml
Calories:	18
Grams fat:	1

HONEY AND LIME DIP FOR FRUIT

Delicious at the beginning or end of a meal, this refreshing dip can be made with lemon or lime. Choose a colourful variety of fruit: strawberries, grapes, pineapple wedges, apple, mango, papaya, pear, peach, melon, sections of orange or other seasonal fresh fruit. Arrange the fruit on a large platter with the dip in the centre and let guests help themselves.

8 fl oz	plain yogurt	250 ml
	Grated peel of 1 lime	
1 tbsp	lime juice	15 ml
3 tbsp	liquid honey	45 ml

Combine all ingredients and mix well; cover and refrigerate overnight (mixture will thicken upon standing). Makes 8 fl oz/250 ml dip (enough for 6 servings).

	Per 1 tbsp/15 ml	4 tbsp/60 ml
Calories:	16	64
Grams fat:	0.2	0.8

Fibre (including 4 oz/125 g fresh fruit):
Good but will vary depending on kind of fruit
Vitamins A and C: Excellent (depending on kind of fruit)

FIRST COURSES

When planning menus, first decide on the main course. If it is low in fat and calories, you can then consider a hearty or cream soup or a more filling first course such as pasta or fish; if the main course is high in fat and calories, choose a light green salad or a clear soup for a first course. Many of the recipes in the book make delicious first courses. Here are some suggestions.

Soups

Any soup recipe in this book can be a first course, but if it is a filling soup, serve in smaller amounts.

Salads

Roasted Red Pepper, Mushroom and Melon Salad (pages 60–1)

Spinach and Red Cabbage Salad with Blue Cheese Dressing (page 61)
Greek Salad (page 77)
Rocket and Radicchio Salad with Balsamic Vinaigrette (page 66)
Pasta Salad with Sweet Peppers and Fresh Dill (pages 80–1)
Julienne Vegetable Salad with Lemon Vinaigrette (page 67)
Artichoke and Tomato Salad (page 63)
Melon with Raspberries (page 200)

Fish

Brochettes of Salmon and Prawn (page 130) (small portions) with Tomato Salsa (page 151) or Dill Mustard Sauce (page 147)
Mussels Sicilian Style (page 122)
Prawns Wrapped with Mangetout (pages 22–3) with Garlic Dip (page 28)

Pasta

Capellini with Clam Sauce and Sweet Red Peppers (page 121)
Linguine with Prawn and Tomato (page 123)
Fettuccine with Fresh Tomatoes and Basil (page 137)
Pasta Salad with Sweet Peppers and Dill (pages 80–1)

Vegetables

Asparagus with Red Pepper Purée (pages 154–5)
Asparagus with Orange Vinaigrette (page 84)
Baked Leeks au Gratin (pages 160–1)
Corn on the Cob (serve just picked, as a first course)
Broccoli Frittata (pages 132–3)

SOUPS

If I had to choose only one type of food to exist on, I would quickly choose soups. A warming soup in winter is the best comfort food of all, and nothing beats a chilled soup in summer to cool and refresh. Any time of year I love to have a large bowl of soup for either lunch or dinner and need nothing more than thick crusty bread, perhaps a wedge of cheese or a salad, and fresh fruit for dessert. Some soups, such as Portuguese Spinach Soup, Summer Garden Italian Soup with Pesto or Split Pea Soup, I can happily eat day after day until a large pot is finished.

Don't forget, when planning your menus, that soups are ideal for lunch or dinner, as either first courses or main courses, or for party fare either after the theatre or cinema.

Soups are often a good source of vitamins, particularly A and C, and of fibre. Cream soups with added milk are usually a good source of calcium, an important addition for adults who don't drink milk and therefore have difficulty meeting their calcium requirements.

Diet Hint: Reducing fat content of soups
When making cream soups, substitute semi-skimmed milk for cream or whole milk and plain low-fat yogurt for sour cream. You can add whipping cream to a hot soup and boil it without the soup curdling, but you cannot do this with the lower-fat substitutes. Here a little care is needed. It is best to warm the milk or yogurt gradually by slowly adding some of the hot mixture to it, then pouring it into the hot soup. The soup can be reheated, but don't let it boil.

See Table E (page 234) for the fat content of milk, yogurt and various creams.

*See page 49 for instructions on cooking beetroot.

BALKAN BEETROOT CREAM SOUP

Save any leftover cooked beetroot for this appetizing chilled soup. On a hot summer evening it's perfect for a light meal, along with a refreshing salad and warm bread.

8 oz	plain yogurt	250 ml
4 fl oz	sour cream	125 ml
8 oz	cottage cheese	250 ml
12 fl oz	semi-skimmed milk	375 ml
4	medium beetroot, cooked, peeled and cut in cubes*	4
2	hard-boiled eggs, peeled and chopped	2
½	unpeeled cucumber, diced	½
8 tbsp	chopped fresh parsley	120 ml
5	sliced radishes	5
3 tbsp	chopped fresh chives or spring onions	45 ml
	Salt and freshly ground pepper	

In blender or food processor, combine sour cream and cottage cheese; mix until smooth (or pass through a sieve). Combine with semi-skimmed milk; refrigerate.

Just before serving, divide beetroot among serving bowls. Stir remaining ingredients into milk mixture and pour over beetroots. Makes 8 large servings (8 fl oz/250 ml each).

Calories per serving: 125
Grams fat per serving: 6.4
Calcium, phosphorus and vitamin C: Good

60-Minute Dinner Party
Chilled Melon and Yogurt
Soup (page 37)
Chicken with Mangetout
(page 96)
Rice
Tarragon Carrots (page 155)
Frozen Lemon Cream
(page 195)

CHILLED MELON AND YOGURT SOUP

A hint of ginger and fresh mint adds zest to this light, refreshing summer soup. Serve it as a first course for brunch, lunch or dinner. Be sure the cantaloupe you use is ripe.

1	ripe cantaloupe melon	1
8 fl oz	plain yogurt	250 ml
3 tbsp	lemon juice	45 ml
$\frac{1}{2}$ tsp	peeled and grated fresh ginger root or $\frac{1}{4}$ tsp/1 ml dried ginger	2 ml
2 tbsp	chopped fresh mint leaves	30 ml

Cut cantaloupe in half and remove seeds. Scoop out pulp into container of food processor or blender and purée. You should have about 12 fl oz/375 ml purée. Add yogurt, lemon juice and ginger; process to mix. Refrigerate until serving.

Serve soup in small bowls, topped with a sprinkling of fresh mint. Makes 4 servings (about 4 fl oz/125 ml each).

Calories per serving: 80
Grams fat per serving: 0.3
Vitamins A and C: Excellent
Calcium: Good

FRESH TOMATO AND DILL BISQUE

Make this soup in the summer and early autumn when fresh dill is available and tomatoes are at their best.

3	large tomatoes, peeled and sliced	3
1	medium onion, sliced	1
1	medium garlic clove, chopped	1
3 tbsp	chopped fresh dill or 2 tsp/10 ml dried dillweed	45 ml
1 tsp	salt	5 ml
$\frac{1}{4}$ tsp	freshly ground pepper	1 ml
4 tbsp	cold water	60 ml
2 oz	cooked macaroni	50 g
8 fl oz	chicken stock	250 ml
6 fl oz	semi-skimmed milk	175 ml
2 tbsp	tomato purée (optional)	30 ml
Garnish		
4 or 5	sprigs fresh dill, chopped	4 or 5
1	large tomato, chopped	1

In saucepan, combine tomatoes, onion, garlic, dill, salt, pepper and cold water. Simmer, covered, for 15 minutes.

Transfer to blender; add macaroni and process for 1 minute. With machine running, add stock, milk and tomato purée (if using). Refrigerate, covered, until thoroughly chilled.

Before serving, taste and adjust seasoning. Garnish each serving with chopped dill and tomato. Makes 4 servings (about 6 fl oz/175 ml each).

Calories per serving: 74
Grams fat per serving: 1.4
Vitamin C: Excellent
Vitamin A: Good

SPLIT PEA SOUP

This is one of our family's favourite soups. We use the leftover bone from a cooked ham. Many cooks add carrots and other vegetables, but we don't—my mother says they take away from the taste of the peas. Don't add any salt until just before serving—there is often enough salt in the ham.

1	ham bone from cooked ham	1
12 oz	split green peas	350 g
3 pts	water	2 L
4	onions, sliced	4
	Salt and freshly ground pepper	

Remove any fat from ham bone, but leave meat. In large saucepan, combine ham bone, peas, water and onions. Bring to a boil and skim off any scum.

Reduce heat and simmer, partially covered, for $1\frac{1}{2}$ to 2 hours or until peas are soft, stirring occasionally. Makes 10 servings (about 6 fl oz/175 ml each).

Calories per serving: 66
Grams fat per serving: 0.2
Fibre: Good

The Taste of Smoked Foods Without Nitrates
The World Cancer Research Fund Guidelines recommend avoiding as much as possible smoked and heavily preserved and salted foods that contain nitrate. (Some nitrate is necessary to prevent botulism.) This means that preserved meats such as bacon, ham and cold cuts should be eaten in moderation or avoided.

One way to have the taste of ham without eating too much of it is to serve Split Pea Soup, which has only small pieces of ham, as well as flavour from the ham bone.

Compare

Fresh Tomato and Dill Bisque made with:	Grams fat/serving
semi-skimmed milk	1.4
whole milk	2.8
single cream	8.7
whipping cream	15.4

GAZPACHO

*Peel cucumber only if skin is tough or waxy.

This cold Spanish soup is perfect for hot summer evenings. It's easy to make in a blender, but tastes best when the vegetables are chopped by hand.

1	garlic clove	1
$\frac{1}{2}$	small onion, quartered	$\frac{1}{2}$
$\frac{1}{2}$	green pepper, seeded and cut in chunks	$\frac{1}{2}$
3	tomatoes, quartered	3
1	cucumber, cut in chunks*	1
2 tbsp	wine vinegar	30 ml
2 tbsp	olive oil	30 ml
4 fl oz	(approx) chicken stock or water (optional)	125 ml
	Salt and freshly ground pepper	

In blender with machine running, drop garlic into feed tube, then add onion. Turn machine off and add green pepper, tomatoes, cucumber, vinegar and oil. Blend just until chopped. If soup is too thick, add up to 4 fl oz/125 ml chicken stock. Cover and store in refrigerator until serving time. Taste, and add salt, pepper and more vinegar if necessary. Serve cold. Makes 6 servings (about 6 fl oz/175 ml each).

Calories per serving: 57
Grams fat per serving: 4
Fibre: Good
Vitamin C: Excellent
Vitamin A: Good

CREAM OF BROCCOLI SOUP

Broccoli is an excellent source of vitamins A and C and of fibre. It's also a brassica vegetable, and people whose diets frequently include brassica vegetables have been shown to have a lower risk of colon cancer. Other brassica vegetables are cabbage, cauliflower, Brussels sprouts, swede, kale and turnips.

This is one of my favourite soups. I like it hot or cold, and sometimes top each serving with a spoonful of sour cream and chopped chives, dill or parsley.

1	large onion, coarsely chopped	1
1	medium carrot, sliced	1
1	small celery stalk (with leaves), sliced	1
1	garlic clove, chopped	1
1¼ pts	chicken stock	750 ml
2 oz	uncooked rice	50 g
10 oz	broccoli, coarsely chopped	300 g
16 fl oz	semi-skimmed milk	500 ml
1 tsp	salt	5 ml
Pinch	cayenne pepper	Pinch

In large saucepan, combine onion, carrot, celery, garlic and chicken stock; bring to a boil. Add rice; cover and simmer for 15 to 20 minutes or until rice is tender. Add broccoli; cover and simmer until broccoli is tender, about 5 minutes. Transfer to blender or food processor and purée (may be done in batches). Return to saucepan; add milk, salt and cayenne. Serve hot. Alternatively, let cool, cover and refrigerate until serving time. Makes 8 servings (6 fl oz/175 ml each).

Calories per serving: 70
Grams fat per serving: 1
Fibre: Good
Vitamins A and C: Excellent

FRESH TOMATO AND BASIL SOUP

This light, flavourful soup is perfect for a first course during tomato season. If fresh basil is not available, use fresh dill; you'll probably want to add more dill than the basil called for here.

½ oz	butter	15 g
1	large garlic clove, chopped	1
1	medium carrot, diced	1
1	medium onion, chopped	1
1½ pts	chicken stock	1 L
1½ lb	peeled and diced ripe tomatoes	675 g
3 tbsp	chopped fresh basil leaves	45 ml
	Salt and freshly ground pepper	

In heavy saucepan, melt butter; stir in garlic, carrot and onion. Cook over medium-low heat until onion is tender. Add stock; cover and simmer for 20 minutes. Stir in tomatoes and simmer for 10 minutes. Just before serving stir in basil and salt and pepper to taste. Makes 6 servings (about 8 fl oz/250 ml each).

Calories per serving: 76
Grams fat per serving: 2.9
Vitamins A and C: Excellent
Niacin: Good

Variation
Seafood Vegetable Soup: After vegetables are tender, add 4 oz/125 g of cooked or raw shelled prawns or scallops, or a combination of both, plus 4 oz/125 g mussels in shell (optional). Simmer for 2 to 3 minutes longer, or until prawns and scallops are opaque and mussel shells open. (Discard any mussel if shell doesn't open.)

SPA VEGETABLE SOUP

One of the easiest and quickest ways of making soup is simply to cook the vegetables in chicken stock. The trick is to have a colourful and interesting variety of vegetables. Here's a suggestion about what vegetables to use, but you may substitute any you have on hand—pumpkin, turnip, celery, potatoes. Add chopped fresh herbs if available.

1¼ pts	chicken stock	750 ml
1	carrot, diagonally sliced	1
3 oz	broccoli florets	75 g
4 oz	cauliflower florets	125 g
4 oz	thinly sliced red cabbage or spinach	125 g
1	spring onion, diagonally sliced	1
	Salt and freshly ground pepper	

In saucepan, bring chicken stock to the boil; add carrot and simmer for 10 minutes. Add remaining vegetables and simmer until tender. Season with salt and pepper to taste. Makes 4 servings (about 8 fl oz/250 ml each).

Calories per serving: 52
Grams fat per serving: 1
Fibre: Good
Vitamins A and C: Good
Niacin: Good

POTAGE VERT

Here is a low-calorie, attractive green vegetable soup that is quick to prepare if you slice the vegetables in a food processor. For a creamy, thick soup, purée in a food processor or blender.

1	large onion, peeled and sliced	1
2	celery stalks, sliced	2
2	garlic cloves, chopped	2
4 oz	green beans, cut in 2 inch/5 cm lengths	125 g
1	large carrot, thinly sliced	1
2¼ pts	chicken stock	1.5 L
10 oz	fresh spinach, washed	300 g
8 oz	frozen peas, thawed	225 g
4	large mushrooms, sliced	4
	Salt and freshly ground pepper	
Pinch	nutmeg	Pinch
5 tbsp	finely chopped fresh parsley	75 ml
1 tsp	dried dillweed or 2 tbsp/30 ml chopped fresh dill	5 ml

In large saucepan, combine onion, celery, garlic, beans, carrot and chicken stock. Bring to a boil; cover, reduce heat and simmer (at a low boil) for 15 minutes or until vegetables are tender. Add spinach, peas and mushrooms; cook until tender, 3 to 5 minutes. Add salt and pepper to taste, nutmeg, parsley and dill. Serve hot. (Soup may also be puréed in food processor or blender and served warm or cold). Makes 8 servings (about 10 fl oz/300 ml each).

Calories per serving: 74
Grams fat per serving: 1.3
Fibre: Excellent
Vitamins A and C and niacin: Excellent
Iron: Good

LEEK AND POTATO SOUP

Variation
Family-Style Leek and Potato
Soup: Omit the cream and
double the potatoes (don't peel
them or you will lose fibre).
Serve without puréeing. Leftovers can be puréed and frozen.
You can also add any other
vegetables such as carrots,
green beans and broccoli to this
soup.

The base for this delicious soup freezes well; just thaw, and
serve hot or cold. For a first course at a dinner party you can
stir in some single cream. For a lunch main course, top soup
with garlic croutons and baby prawns and chopped chives or
spring onions.

6	medium leeks	6
1	garlic clove, chopped	1
4	medium potatoes, peeled, cubed	4
$3\frac{1}{4}$ pts	chicken stock	2 L
8 fl oz	single cream (optional)	250 ml
	Salt and freshly ground pepper	
3 tbsp	fresh parsley or chives, finely chopped	45 ml

Trim all but about 2 inches/5 cm of green part from leeks.
Cut lengthwise halfway into white part. Spread apart and
wash under cold running water. Slice thinly by hand or in
food processor.

In saucepan, combine leeks, garlic, potatoes and chicken
stock; simmer, partially covered, for 30 minutes or until
vegetables are tender. Purée in blender or food processor.
(Soup can be prepared ahead to this point; let cool, transfer
to freezer containers and freeze. Reheat gently before
continuing with recipe.)

Just before serving, reheat soup; add cream (if you are
using it), and salt and pepper to taste. Remove from heat.
Sprinkle with parsley. Makes 12 servings (about 8 fl oz/250 ml
each).

Calories per serving: 91
Grams fat per serving: 3
Vitamin C and niacin: Good

SUMMER GARDEN ITALIAN SOUP WITH PESTO

Pesto, a pungent Italian sauce made with fresh basil and garlic, adds exquisite flavour to soups, pasta and vegetable dishes. This version has less oil than most, without any loss in flavour. Add pesto sauce directly to soup before serving, or top each serving with a spoonful.

8 oz	dried white beans	225 g
1 tbsp	vegetable oil	15 ml
2	onions, coarsely chopped	2
3	large tomatoes, peeled, seeded and chopped, or 16 oz/450 g canned, chopped	3
4	carrots, thinly sliced	4
2	potatoes, coarsely chopped	2
4	leeks (white part only), coarsely chopped (optional)	4
2	large celery stalks (with leaves), coarsely chopped	2
8 oz	sliced green beans	225 g
1	medium courgette, coarsely chopped	1
2 oz	broken egg noodles or spaghetti	50 g
	Salt and freshly ground pepper	
Pesto		
2	large garlic cloves	2
12 tbsp	fresh basil leaves (or fresh parsley leaves, plus 2 tsp/10 ml dried basil)	175 ml
2 oz	grated Parmesan cheese	50 g
2 tbsp	olive oil	30 ml
4 tbsp	(approx) hot soup liquid	60 ml

Soak beans in water overnight and drain, or cover beans with cold water and bring to a boil, remove from heat and let stand for 1 hour, then drain.

In saucepan, combine beans with enough water to cover; bring to a boil and boil hard for 10 minutes. Reduce heat and simmer, covered, until beans are tender, about 1 hour; drain.

Pasta with Pesto Sauce: If making pesto to serve with pasta, use pasta cooking liquid instead of soup liquid and add enough to make sauce thick, yet pourable. Spoon about 1 tbsp/15 ml over each serving of hot drained pasta and toss to mix.

Compare
This pesto sauce has less than half the amount of fat of most pesto recipes.

In a frying pan, heat oil over medium heat; add onions and cook, stirring, until tender, 6 to 8 minutes. Add tomatoes (if using fresh) and cook until soft, 3 to 4 minutes.

In large pot, bring 3½ pts/2 L water to a boil. Add carrots, potatoes, leeks, celery, onion mixture and tomatoes (if using canned); simmer for 15 minutes.

Add green beans, courgettes, egg noodles and cooked white beans; simmer until vegetables are tender, 10 to 15 minutes, adding more water if needed. Add salt and pepper to taste.

Pesto: In food processor, combine garlic and basil; process until chopped. Add Parmesan and olive oil and process until smooth. Add enough warm soup liquid to make mixture the consistency of mayonnaise.

Ladle soup into bowls. Top each serving with a spoonful of pesto. Makes 10 servings (about 11 fl oz/325 ml each).

Calories per serving: 162
Grams fat per serving: 5
Fibre: Excellent
Vitamins A and C: Excellent
Iron and niacin: Good

SEAFOOD CHOWDER

Serve as a main course, along with crusty rolls and a tossed green salad, for a dinner buffet or an after-theatre party. You can make it early in the day to give the flavours a chance to develop. To save time, chop onions, celery and carrots in a food processor.

½ oz	butter	15 g
1	large onion, chopped	1
16 fl oz	chicken stock or clam juice	500 ml
2	chopped celery sticks	2
3	carrots, coarsely chopped	3
1 tsp	salt	5 ml
	Freshly ground pepper	
1 lb	haddock fillets	450 g
16 fl oz	whole milk	500 ml
5 tbsp	plain flour	75 ml
1	can (5 oz/142 g) clams, undrained (optional)	1
4 oz	cooked small prawns or lobster meat	125 g

In large saucepan or soup kettle, melt butter; add onions and cook over low heat for a few minutes until soft. Stir in chicken stock, celery, carrots, salt, and pepper to taste. Bring to a boil; reduce heat and simmer, uncovered, for 20 minutes or until carrots are tender. Add fillets, cover and cook for 5 minutes longer. (The chowder may be prepared ahead to this point and frozen; thaw and reheat before continuing with recipe.)

Stir about half of the milk into the flour to make a smooth mixture. Gradually stir mixture into soup, then stir in remaining milk and simmer until soup thickens slightly. Just before serving, stir in clams and prawns; heat through. Taste and adjust seasonings. Makes 6 servings (about 10 fl oz/300 ml each).

Calories per serving: 225
Grams fat per serving: 6
Calcium: Good
Vitamin A and niacin: Excellent

VEGETABLE BORSCHT

Serve small portions of this beautifully coloured soup for a
first course, or larger servings for a main course. Any leftover
soup may be frozen.

1	onion, chopped	1
2	large fresh beetroots, peeled and chopped	2
1	medium carrot, sliced	1
1	large potato, peeled and cubed	1
1½ pts	beef or chicken stock	1 L
¼	small head cabbage, shredded	¼
1	tomato, chopped	1
2 tbsp	chopped fresh parsley	30 ml
½ tsp	dried dillweed	2 ml
1 tsp	salt	5 ml
	Freshly ground pepper	
1 tsp	lemon juice	5 ml
Garnish		
3 tbsp	sour cream or plain yogurt	45 ml

In large saucepan, combine onion, beetroots, carrot,
potato and stock. Bring to a boil; cover and simmer for 30
minutes, skimming foam if necessary. Add cabbage, tomato,
parsley and dill; simmer for 30 minutes longer, or until
vegetables are tender. Season with salt, pepper to taste and
lemon juice. Top each serving with 1 tsp/5 ml of sour cream.
Makes 8 servings (8 fl oz/250 ml each).

Calories per serving: 53
Grams fat per serving: 1.4
Fibre: Good
Vitamins A and C: Good

TOMATO AND BEAN CHOWDER

This comforting soup is hearty enough for a cold winter day, yet light enough for a summer supper.

4	onions, finely chopped	4
2 tsp	chilli powder	10 ml
1	green pepper, seeded and chopped	1
2	cans tomatoes, undrained	2
1½ pts	beef or vegetable stock	1 L
1	can (15.2 oz/432 g) red kidney beans, drained	1
1	can (15.2 oz/432 g) chick peas, drained	1
	Salt and freshly ground pepper	
Garnish		
8 tbsp	finely chopped fresh parsley	125 ml

In large, heavy saucepan, combine onions, chilli powder, green pepper, tomatoes and stock; bring to boil, reduce heat and simmer for 15 minutes. Break up tomatoes with back of spoon. Add drained beans and chick peas; simmer for 10 minutes. Add salt and pepper to taste. Garnish each serving with a sprinkling of parsley. Makes 10 servings (8 fl oz/250 ml each).

Calories per serving: 198
Grams fat per serving: 2.6
Fibre: Excellent
Vitamin C: Excellent
Iron, vitamin A, phosphorus and niacin: Good

TRI-COLOUR BEAN SOUP

Rush-Hour Family Dinner
Tri-Colour Bean Soup (page 51)
Spinach Supper Salad
(page 75)
Wholewheat rolls
Fresh fruit

*If unavailable, substitute
kidney beans, baby lima beans,
black-eyed beans or flageolets.

This hearty soup is a meal on its own. Serve with homemade bread and a crisp salad.

2	large onions, sliced	2
3	garlic cloves, chopped	3
1½ pts	water	1 L
2	potatoes, cubed	2
3	carrots, cut in ¼ inch/5 mm slices	3
1	can (15.2 oz/432 g) pinto beans, drained*	1
1	can (15.2 oz/432 g) kidney beans, baby lima beans, black-eyed beans or flageolets, drained	1
1	can (15.2 oz/432 g) chick peas, drained	1
1 tsp	oregano	5 ml
2 tsp	basil	10 ml
	Salt and freshly ground pepper	

In large saucepan, combine onions, garlic, water, potatoes and carrots; bring to a boil, cover and simmer for 20 minutes or until vegetables are tender. Add all beans, oregano, basil, and salt and pepper to taste. Simmer for 5 to 10 minutes to blend flavours. Makes 12 servings (8 fl oz/250 ml each).

Calories per serving: 120
Grams fat per serving: 1.6
Fibre: Excellent
Iron and vitamin A: Good

PORTUGUESE SPINACH SOUP

*Chorizo sausages are available in many delicatessens. Sweet means they are not hot and spicy. If chorizo sausages aren't available, use a small pepperoni instead.

For a very low-fat diet, omit oil. Soup will taste fine.

Beetroot Greens
Don't throw out the beetroot tops. Cooked beetroot greens are an excellent source of vitamin A and folic acid, and a good source of vitamin C, riboflavin, calcium and fibre. They're delicious steamed, boiled or used instead of spinach leaves in Portuguese Spinach Soup (page 52).

Beetroot greens are best when cooked fresh from the garden or within a day or two of picking. They are prepared and cooked like spinach, but require a longer cooking time.

To prepare and cook beetroot greens: Cut off and discard tough stems or blemished leaves. Either steam in covered steamer over simmering water for 10 to 15 minutes or until wilted and tender, or boil, covered, in $\frac{1}{2}$ inch/1 cm of water in large saucepan for 10 to 15 minutes or until tender. Drain, and season with salt, pepper, lemon juice and a dab of butter.

This popular Portuguese soup is usually made with collard greens but as they can be difficult to find I've used spinach. You can also use beet greens or chard leaves.

5	large potatoes, peeled and coarsely chopped	5
1	large carrot, cut in thin slices	1
$2\frac{1}{4}$ pts	water	1.5 L
10 oz	fresh spinach	300 g
2 oz	chorizo* (sweet smoked pork sausage), about $3\frac{1}{2}$ inches/9 cm long	50 g
2 tbsp	olive oil	30 ml
2 tsp	salt	10 ml

In saucepan, combine potatoes, carrot and water; simmer over medium heat until tender. Use a hand-held blender to purée in the saucepan until smooth. (Alternatively, use slotted spoon to transfer potatoes and carrots to food processor, then blend until smooth. Return potato mixture to saucepan with cooking liquid and stir until combined.)

Thinly slice spinach leaves into $\frac{1}{8}$ inch/2 mm or smaller strips. (Roll up 4 or 5 leaves and slice crosswise.)

Peel casing from sausage; slice sausage as thinly as possible ($\frac{1}{16}$ inch/1 mm thick). Add sliced leaves and sausage to soup; stir. Simmer, uncovered, for 10 minutes. Add oil and salt. If soup is too thick, add more water. Makes 10 servings (8 fl oz/250 ml each).

Calories per serving: 185
Grams fat per serving: 6.7
Fibre: Excellent
Vitamins A and C: Excellent
Thiamin, calcium and iron: Good

RED LENTIL SOUP

Serve this easy-to-make soup with grilled cheese sandwiches or a salad for a quick meal. Be sure to use red lentils, not brown ones, in this soup.

8 oz	dried red lentils	225 g
3	onions, coarsely chopped	3
2 pts	water	1.25 L
1	bay leaf	1
1	large garlic clove, chopped	1
1 tsp	dried thyme (or 1 tbsp/15 ml chopped fresh)	5 ml
3	carrots, scraped and thinly sliced	3
3 tbsp	chopped fresh parsley	45 ml
	Salt and freshly ground pepper	

Wash and drain lentils. In large saucepan, combine lentils, onions, water, bay leaf and garlic. Cover and simmer for 1 hour. Add thyme and carrots; simmer, covered, for 30 minutes longer, or until carrots are tender and lentils are soft. Remove bay leaf. Add parsley, and salt and pepper to taste. Serve hot. Makes 8 servings (6 fl oz/175 ml each).

Calories per serving: 96
Grams fat per serving: 0.9
Fibre: Good
Vitamin A: Excellent

Brown or Red Lentils—Is there a difference?

Yes. When cooked, red lentils are soft, while brown lentils retain their shape. Use red lentils for soups, and dishes (such as burgers) where you want the lentils to be soft. Use brown lentils in salads, or in dishes where you want the lentils to retain their shape.

When cooked in a soup, red lentils turn an attractive yellow. Brown lentils are unappealing in soups, unless used in a small amount and combined with other vegetables.

Because lentils are a good source of protein they are often included in meatless meals. 6 oz/175 g of lentils are an excellent source of fibre.

FISH CHOWDER, FAMILY STYLE

Super Supper
Fish Chowder, Family Style
(page 54)
Wholewheat rolls
Tossed salad
Fresh fruit

Any fresh or frozen fillets can be used in this recipe, but try monkfish if it's available.

1 oz	butter	25 g
1	onion, finely chopped	1
3	potatoes, diced	3
1	carrot, finely chopped	1
16 fl oz	water	500 ml
16 fl oz	milk	500 ml
1 lb	monkfish or other fish fillets (fresh or frozen)	450 g
5 oz	sweetcorn	150 g
	Salt and freshly ground pepper	
	Chopped fresh parsley	

In heavy saucepan, melt butter; add onion, potatoes and carrot, and cook over medium heat, stirring occasionally, for 5 minutes. Add water; cover and simmer until vegetables are nearly tender, about 15 minutes.

Stir in milk, fish (if using monkfish, cut into chunks) and sweetcorn; simmer for 5 to 10 minutes, or until fish flakes and is opaque. Add salt, pepper, and parsley to taste. Makes about 2½ pts/1.5L. 4 large servings of 12 fl oz/375 ml each..

Calories per serving: 258
Grams fat per serving: 8
Fibre: Good
Vitamins A and C: Excellent
Calcium, phosphorus and niacin: Good

CURRIED APPLE AND COURGETTE SOUP

This light cream soup has a lovely delicate flavour. It's a good choice for a first course at a dinner party.

½ oz	margarine or butter	15 g
1	large onion, chopped	1
1	apple, peeled, cored and chopped	1
1 to 2 tsp	curry powder	5 to 10 ml
1½ pts	chicken stock	1 L
2 oz	uncooked rice	50 g
8 oz	diced unpeeled courgette	225 g
½ tsp	salt	2 ml
8 fl oz	semi-skimmed milk	250 ml

In saucepan, melt butter; sauté onion and apple until soft. Sprinkle with curry powder; cook, stirring, for a few seconds. Pour in chicken stock; bring to a boil. Add rice, courgette and salt. Cover and cook until rice and courgette are tender, about 30 minutes. Pour into blender and blend until smooth. Return to pan and add milk. Heat through. Serve hot. Makes 8 servings (6 fl oz/175 ml each).

Calories per serving: 79
Grams fat per serving: 1.9
Niacin: Good

CHICKEN AND LEEK CHOWDER

Here's a delicately flavoured yet hearty soup. For a stew, simply thicken liquid with flour and add dumplings to top.

1	chicken (3 lb/1.5 kg)	1
1	onion, coarsely chopped	1
1	celery stalk, chopped	1
3¼ pts	water	2 L
10	black peppercorns	10
4	large leeks	4
2	large potatoes, diced	2
3	medium carrots, sliced	3
2	large celery stalks, chopped	2
1 tbsp	chopped fresh thyme leaves or 1 tsp/5 ml dried	15 ml
1 tbsp	chopped fresh tarragon leaves or 1 tsp/5 ml dried	15 ml
1 tbsp	chopped fresh rosemary leaves or 1 tsp/5 ml dried	15 ml
2	bay leaves	2
5 oz	sweetcorn (frozen or canned)	150 g
8 oz	lima beans (frozen or canned)	225 g
1 oz	vermicelli or broken spaghetti	25 g
½ oz	butter	15 g
12 fl oz	milk	375 ml
5 tbsp	plain flour	75 ml
12 tbsp	chopped fresh parsley	175 ml
2 tsp	salt	10 ml
	Freshly ground pepper	

Remove as much fat as possible from chicken, and discard. In large saucepan or soup kettle, combine chicken, onion, 1 celery stalk, water and peppercorns. Bring to a boil; reduce heat, partially cover and simmer for 1 to 1½ hours or until chicken is cooked. Leave to cool.

Remove chicken from pan and discard skin and bones; cut meat into bite-size pieces and set aside. Strain liquid and refrigerate. When cold, remove hardened fat from surface.

Trim leeks, leaving about 3 inches/8 cm, or tender part, of greens attached. Cut stalks in half lengthwise and wash

Opposite:
Melon and Bean Salad
(page 72)

thoroughly under running water, holding leaves apart. Slice crosswise into $\frac{1}{2}$-inch/1 cm slices. In large saucepan, combine leeks, potatoes, carrots and reserved chicken stock (from cooking chicken); bring to a boil and simmer for 15 minutes, stirring occasionally.

Add chopped celery and chicken meat to soup. Add thyme, tarragon, rosemary and bay leaves; simmer for 10 minutes. Add sweetcorn, beans and vermicelli or broken spaghetti; cook for 10 minutes longer, or until vegetables are tender.

Just before serving remove bay leaves and add butter. Stir enough of the milk into the flour to make a smooth, thin paste; gradually add to soup, stirring continously. Add remaining milk, parsley, salt, and pepper to taste. Makes 10 large servings.

Calories per serving: 232
Grams fat per serving: 5.7
Fibre: Good
Niacin, vitamins A and C: Excellent
Iron: Good

Opposite:
Spinach and Red Cabbage Salad (page 51) with Blue Cheese Dressing (page 34)

SWEETCORN AND TOMATO CHOWDER WITH TARRAGON

*For a completely different but appealing flavour, substitute 1 tsp/5 ml each curry powder and cumin for the tarragon.

**1lb/450 g of corn on the cob will yield 10 oz/300 g of sweetcorn

Fresh tarragon is a delicious addition to this soup. If it isn't available, but other fresh herbs are, use them instead (try basil, rosemary or oregano). If you can't find any fresh herbs, use dried tarragon.* Serve soup hot or cold.

½ oz	butter	15 g
½	onion, chopped	½
1	garlic clove, chopped	1
2 tbsp	plain flour	30 ml
1	can (14 oz/400 g) plum tomatoes (undrained)	1
2	potatoes, diced	2
8 fl oz	chicken stock	250 ml
16 fl oz	milk	500 ml
10 oz	sweetcorn (canned, frozen or from cooked cob)**	300 g
1 tbsp	chopped fresh tarragon	15 ml
2 tbsp	chopped fresh parsley	30 ml
2 tbsp	chopped fresh chives or spring onions	30 ml
	Salt and freshly ground pepper	

In heavy saucepan, melt butter; add onion and garlic and cook over medium heat until tender. Sprinkle flour into pan and mix well. Stir in tomatoes and bring to a boil, stirring. Add potatoes and stock; boil gently for 15 minutes, or until potatoes are tender.

In separate saucepan or in microwave oven, heat milk until hot but not boiling; pour into tomato mixture and stir in sweetcorn.

Just before serving, stir in tarragon, parsley, chives, and salt and pepper to taste. Makes 10 servings (6 fl oz/175 ml each).

Calories per serving: 88
Grams fat per serving: 2.3
Fibre: Good
Vitamin C: Excellent
Vitamin A: Good

CREAMED CUCUMBER BISQUE

A refreshing beginning to a dinner or a picnic, this cream soup is low in calories and fat.

1	cucumber	1
½ tsp	salt	2 ml
8 fl oz	semi-skimmed milk	250 ml
8 fl oz	chicken stock	250 ml
8 fl oz	plain low fat yogurt	250 ml
2 tbsp	spring onions or fresh chives, finely chopped	30 ml
4 tbsp	chopped fresh parsley	60 ml
	Freshly ground pepper	
Garnish		
	Thin slices of unpeeled cucumber	
	Cooked prawns (optional)	

Peel cucumber only if skin is tough; remove seeds and chop cucumber by hand or in food processor. Place in colander; sprinkle with salt. Let drain for 30 minutes; pat dry.

In a large bowl, combine milk, chicken stock, onion, parsley, pepper to taste and cucumber. Refrigerate for 2 to 8 hours. Taste and adjust seasoning if necessary. To serve, ladle into bowls; garnish with cucumber slice and a few prawns if using. Makes 4 servings (about 8 fl oz/250 ml each).

Calories per serving: 46
Grams fat per serving: 1.1

SALADS

S alads are achieving a new status in our meals and deservedly so. Rock-hard tomatoes and flavourless iceberg lettuce are finally being pushed aside by crisp Frisée and tender buttery Lollo Biondo lettuce. We now have so many wonderful fresh ingredients to work with that there has been a break-through in imaginative combinations of food—the Melon and Bean Salad (page 72) is absolutely delicious. In fact, we could feast on salads for months and never taste the same one twice. Red radicchio and chinese leaves are special treats to excite your palate. Pasta salads (now more imaginative than macaroni with mayonnaise), Greek Salad, Chick Pea with Red Onion and Tomato, plus many others, are delicious as a main course as well as a side salad.

Moreover, health-conscious gourmets realize that salads are a good way to get fibre, vitamins and minerals into our diet. When combined with high-fibre vegetables, such as spinach, beans and chick peas, and tossed with a low-fat dressing, such as Yogurt and Basil (page 85) or Blue Cheese Dressing (page 84), they are low in calories and fat, and high in fibre. This follows the World Cancer Research Fund's recommendations for a low-fat, high-fibre diet.

ROASTED RED PEPPER, MUSHROOM AND MELON SALAD

Roasted peppers have a rich, delicious taste and a soft, yet still firm, texture. If time is short, use the peppers raw. This salad is spectacular as an appetizer or for lunch. Increase the prawns and serve as a main-course salad for a light supper.

1	large sweet red pepper	1
1	head Lollo Biondo lettuce	1
1	honeydew melon or cantaloupe	1
12	mushrooms	12
2	tomatoes, sliced	2
8 oz	cooked prawns (optional)	225 g
8 fl oz	Orange Vinaigrette (page 84)	250 ml

Place red pepper on a baking sheet; roast in 375°F/190°C/Gas Mark 5 oven for 18 minutes; turn and roast on other side for 18 minutes longer, or until pepper is soft and blistered. Place pepper in paper or plastic bag; close bag and let pepper steam for 10 minutes. Using fingers and small knife, peel skin from pepper (it should come off easily); seed pepper and cut into strips.

Wash lettuce leaves; dry in spinner or with paper towels and refrigerate until needed. Cut melon in half; discard seeds. Peel and cut melon into wedges. Slice mushrooms.

Line 8 individual salad plates with lettuce leaves. Arrange wedges of melon in centre; place red pepper strips on top of melon, mushrooms on one side, tomato slices on other and prawns (if using) over remaining lettuce. Drizzle Orange Vinaigrette over each salad. Makes 8 appetizer servings.

Calories per serving: 82
Grams fat per serving: 0.8
Fibre: Good
Vitamin C: Excellent
Vitamin A, iron and niacin: Good

SPINACH AND RED CABBAGE SALAD WITH BLUE CHEESE DRESSING

Red cabbage on dark green spinach is a striking colour combination. Team it with Blue Cheese Dressing (page 84) to add extra tang and a creamy texture.

5 oz	packed spinach leaves	150 g
8 oz	grated red cabbage	225 g
5 fl oz	Blue Cheese Dressing	150 ml

Wash spinach; discard tough ends and tear large leaves into 2 or 3 pieces. Just before serving, toss spinach with cabbage and dressing. (Alternatively, line individual plates with spinach, arrange cabbage in rings on top. Place spoonful of dressing in centre of each plate.) Makes 4 servings.

Calories per serving: 56
Grams fat per serving: 2
Fibre: Good
Vitamins A and C: Excellent

Menu-Planning Tip for Busy Cooks
Once a week, make a large amount of a hearty soup, such as Tri-Colour Bean Soup (page 51), Summer Garden Italian Vegetable Soup with Pesto (page 46) or Seafood Chowder (page 48), and a salad that keeps well, such as Bermuda Bean Salad (pages 78–9). Tabbouleh (page 64) or Chick Pea Salad with Red Onion and Tomato (page 78). Along with thick fresh bread or toast, you'll be ready for rush-hour meals. Or serve either the salad or the soup with open grilled sandwiches, such as mozzarella on wholewheat rolls sprinkled with oregano for a fast, nutritious meal.

BROCCOLI BUFFET SALAD

Winter Family Supper
Broccoli Buffet Salad (page 62)
Omelette à la Jardinière
(page 135)
Old-Fashioned Molasses Bread
(page 180)
Cinnamon Apple sauce
(page 219)

Serve this colourful winter salad as a first course, or as a main course with an omelette, soup or grilled meat or chicken. It's ideal for a buffet table because you can make it ahead. For a variation, make the salad with Tomato French Dressing (page 86) instead of the vinaigrette.

1 lb	broccoli	450 g
1	red onion, thinly sliced and separated into rings	1
4 oz	small mushrooms	125 g
4 oz	feta cheese, crumbled	125 g
2 tbsp	toasted sliced almonds	30 ml
Vinaigrette Dressing		
2 tbsp	olive oil	30 ml
2 tbsp	lemon juice	30 ml
3 tbsp	water	45 ml
1	garlic clove, chopped	1
$\frac{1}{2}$ tsp	oregano	2 ml
	Salt and freshly ground pepper	

Trim ends of broccoli. Cut into florets. Peel stalks and cut into 1 inch/2.5 cm long strips about $\frac{1}{4}$ inch/6 mm wide.

In large pot of rapidly boiling water, cook broccoli for 2 minutes; drain, and refresh under cold running water to prevent further cooking and to set colour; drain and dry with paper towels. (If preparing a day in advance, do not cook broccoli; use raw.)

In salad bowl, toss broccoli with onion, mushrooms and cheese.

Vinaigrette Dressing: Combine oil, lemon juice, water, garlic and oregano; mix well. Pour over vegetables and toss well. Season with salt and pepper to taste. Toss again. Sprinkle almonds over top. Serve immediately, or cover and refrigerate for up to 3 hours. Stir before serving. Makes about 8 servings.

Calories per serving: 120
Grams fat per serving: 7.8
Fibre: Excellent
Calcium, phosphorus, riboflavin and niacin: Good
Vitamins A and C: Excellent

ARTICHOKE AND TOMATO SALAD

Tasty chunks of artichoke heart combine with cucumbers, tomatoes and spring onions for a sensational summer salad. Serve with soup or cheese and fresh bread for lunch or supper.

2 tbsp	red wine vinegar	30 ml
½ tsp	Dijon mustard	2 ml
1	garlic clove, chopped	1
4 tbsp	vegetable or olive oil	60 ml
4	spring onions, chopped	4
1	cucumber, cut in chunks	1
5	tomatoes, coarsely chopped	5
1	can (14 oz/400 g) artichoke hearts, drained and quartered	1
2	hard-boiled eggs, chopped	2
	Salt and freshly ground pepper	
	Lemon juice	

In large salad bowl, mix together vinegar, mustard and garlic. Gradually whisk in oil. Add following ingredients in layers; onions, cucumber, tomatoes and artichokes. Sprinkle eggs over top. Cover and refrigerate.

About 15 minutes before serving, toss salad and add salt, pepper and lemon juice to taste. Makes 6 large servings.

Calories per serving: 134
Grams fat per serving: 10
Fibre: Good
Vitamin C: Excellent
Vitamin A: Good

	Per 3½ oz/100 g
Compare	Grams fibre
Lettuce (iceberg, cos)	1.5
Cabbage (red, green or Savoy)	3.4
Spinach	3.9

TABBOULEH

This Mediterranean salad is one of my favourite summer salads. It's delicious as part of a salad plate for picnics or lunches, and keeps well in the refrigerator. Bulgur, or cracked wheat, adds a nutty flavour and texture, and fresh mint lends a special touch. If mint isn't in season, simply omit it.

6 oz	bulgur (cracked wheat)	175 g
5 tbsp	olive oil	75 ml
5 tbsp	lemon juice	75 ml
1 bunch	spring onions, finely chopped	1 bunch
2 oz	chopped fresh parsley	50 g
4 tbsp	chopped fresh mint	60 ml
3	tomatoes, diced	3
1	cucumber, peeled, seeded and chopped	1
1 tsp	salt	5 ml
	Freshly ground pepper	

Soak bulgur for 1 hour in enough warm water to cover, drain well. Toss with oil, lemon juice, onions, parsley, mint, tomatoes and cucumber. Cover and refrigerate for at least 1 hour or overnight. Add salt, and pepper to taste. Makes 10 servings.

Calories per serving: 148
Grams fat per serving: 7
Fibre: Good
Vitamins A and C: Excellent

Picnic Salad Supper
White Kidney Bean Salad (page 74)
Pasta Salad with Sweet Peppers and Dill (page 80)
Tabbouleh (page 64)
Wholewheat pitta bread
Fresh peaches

Bulgur and Cracked Wheat
Bulgur and cracked wheat add a new dimension in texture, a nutty flavour, good nutrients and fibre to dishes. They are both made from wheat grains and can be used interchangeably in most recipes. Cracked wheat is basically made from wheat grains that have been cracked, then coarsely milled. Bulgur is made from wheat grains that have been crushed, then either parboiled (European) or steamed (American), then dried.

Bulgur and cracked wheat are available in some supermarkets, but you can always find them in health food stores. Use in salads (Tabbouleh) or stuffings, or mix with other grains or vegetables. To cook, combine with twice as much water as grain and simmer bulgur for about 15 minutes, cracked wheat for about 25 minutes, or until tender but not mushy.

DANISH CUCUMBER SALAD

The Danes serve this salad often, especially with chicken or as a topping for open sandwiches. Sprinkling the cucumbers with salt draws out the water and makes the cucumbers crisp. The dressing has virtually no fat. When I had this dish in Denmark, it was beautifully garnished with blue cornflowers.

2	cucumbers	2
1 tbsp	salt	15 ml
7 oz	granulated sugar	200 g
8 fl oz	vinegar (white wine or cider)	250 ml
	Salt and freshly ground pepper	
	Chopped fresh dill	

Thinly slice unpeeled cucumbers and place in bowl or sieve. Sprinkle with salt and let stand for 1 hour. Pour off liquid and pat dry; transfer to bowl.

In a small saucepan or microwave-safe dish, combine sugar and vinegar; stir over low heat or heat in microwave until sugar is dissolved; remove from heat and let cool. Pour over cucumbers; let stand for 30 to 60 minutes. Drain cucumbers; season with salt and pepper to taste. Garnish with chopped dill. Makes 6 to 8 servings.

Calories per serving: 40
Grams fat per serving: trace
Vitamin C: Good

ROCKET AND RADICCHIO SALAD WITH BALSAMIC VINAIGRETTE

Easter Luncheon
Melon with lime
Hard Boiled Eggs with Curry
Sauce over Rice (page 98)
Tossed salad greens with
Balsamic Vinaigrette (page 66).
Rhubarb Crumb Pie
(pages 216–17)

*Available in some
supermarkets and most
speciality food stores.

Rocket, or Arugula as it is also known, is a tender lettuce with a delightful buttery-nutty flavour—it's very special and very expensive. If Arugula isn't available, you can use watercress. Radicchio, a red leaf chicory, is much like a small cabbage in appearance. Together they make an elegant salad. The flavours are wonderful, so it isn't necessary to add a lot of other ingredients.

1	small head radicchio	1
1	bunch rocket or watercress	1
1	lettuce	1
1	orange (optional)	1
4 tbsp	coarsely chopped fresh parsley	60 ml
2 tbsp	balsamic vinegar*	30 ml
2 tbsp	olive oil	30 ml
	Salt and freshly ground pepper	

Separate salad leaves and wash thoroughly. Spin, or pat dry on paper towels. Wrap and refrigerate until serving time. Cut off rind and white pith from orange (if using), cut into thin slices.

Just before serving, tear lettuces into large pieces. Combine with orange slices in glass salad bowl. (Alternatively, arrange lettuce on individual salad plates. Arrange orange slices on top.) Sprinkle with parsley, vinegar, oil, salt and pepper, and toss to mix. Makes 6 servings.

Calories per serving: 56
Grams fat per serving: 4
Vitamin C: Excellent
Vitamin A: Good

JULIENNE VEGETABLE SALAD WITH LEMON VINAIGRETTE

White or yellow turnip or tender parsnips cut into julienne, or matchstick-size, strips are delicious additions to this salad.

3	carrots, cut in julienne strips	3
3	courgettes, cut in julienne strips	3
4 oz	green beans in 1½ inch/4 cm lengths	125 g
3	sticks of celery, cut in julienne strips	3
	Salt and freshly ground pepper	

Lemon Vinaigrette

1 tbsp	olive or walnut oil	15 ml
4 tbsp	lemon juice	60 ml
2 tbsp	chopped spring onion tops or fresh chives	30 ml
1	garlic clove, chopped	1

In bowl, combine carrot, courgette, green beans and celery.

Lemon Vinaigrette: In small bowl, combine oil, lemon juice, parsley, green onions and garlic; mix thoroughly. Pour over vegetables and toss to mix. Add salt and pepper to taste. Cover and refrigerate until serving. Makes 6 servings.

Calories per serving: 45
Grams fat per serving: 2.4
Fibre: Good
Vitamins A and C: Excellent

COLESLAW WITH APPLE AND ONION

To reduce the fat content and to give a lighter flavour and texture, substitute low-fat yogurt for mayonnaise in salad dressing recipes, or use half yogurt and half sour cream.

This is a good everyday summer salad, using new-crop, crisp cabbage, and a fine winter salad when lettuce and tomatoes aren't plentiful or sweet.

1 lb	finely shredded cabbage	450 g
1	medium carrot, grated	1
$\frac{1}{2}$	green pepper, chopped	$\frac{1}{2}$
1	apple, chopped	1
2	spring onions, chopped	2
	Salt and freshly ground pepper	

Yogurt Dressing

3 tbsp	plain yogurt	45 ml
2 tbsp	sour cream	30 ml
1 tbsp	mayonnaise	15 ml
1 tsp	lemon juice	5 ml
$\frac{1}{4}$ tsp	dillweed	1 ml

In serving bowl, combine cabbage, carrot, green pepper, apple and onions.

Yogurt Dressing: Combine yogurt, sour cream, mayonnaise, lemon juice and dill; mix well. Pour over salad and toss to mix. Add salt and pepper to taste. Makes 4 servings.

Calories per serving: 70
Grams fat per serving: 2.7
Fibre: Good
Vitamin A: Excellent
Vitamin C: Good

TOMATO RAITA

Raita is an East Indian type of salad. Delicious with curries, it adds a colourful note to the meal.

1	medium cucumber	1
1 tsp	salt	5 ml
2	medium tomatoes	2
1 tbsp	finely chopped onion	15 ml
8 fl oz	plain yogurt	250 ml
4 tbsp	chopped fresh parsley	60 ml
2 tbsp	chopped fresh coriander	30 ml
1 tsp	cumin	5 ml

Peel cucumber. Cut in half lengthwise and remove seeds. Cut into thin slices by hand or in food processor; sprinkle with salt and let stand for about 40 minutes. Drain cucumber, squeezing slightly to remove excess liquid.

Core tomatoes; cut into $\frac{1}{2}$inch/1 cm cubes. Toss together tomatoes, cucumber and onion; drain off any liquid. Combine yogurt, parsley, coriander and cumin; pour over vegetables and mix with a spoon. Cover, and refrigerate until ready to serve. Makes 4 servings.

Calories per serving: 59
Grams fat per serving: 0.3
Calcium: Good
Vitamin C: Excellent
Vitamin A: Good

RED POTATO SALAD WITH SOUR CREAM AND CHIVES

Red-skinned potatoes add colour, but any kind of new potato can be used. Be sure to leave the skin on, for additional flavour and fibre. Sour cream and yogurt combine to make a light yet creamy dressing that is much lower in fat than traditional mayonnaise.

6	medium-large red-skinned potatoes	6
4 fl oz	sour cream	125 ml
4 fl oz	plain yogurt	125 ml
4 tbsp	finely chopped fresh chives or spring onions	60 ml
1 tsp	salt	5 ml
	Freshly ground pepper	

Scrub potatoes (don't peel). If large, cut in half or in quarters. Boil potatoes in their skins until fork-tender; drain. Shake pan over medium heat for a few seconds to dry potatoes. Cut into ½ inch/1 cm cubes; let cool.

Combine sour cream, yogurt and chives; toss with potatoes. Add salt, and pepper to taste. Refrigerate until serving. Makes 10 servings.

Calories per serving: 130
Grams fat per serving: 4
Fibre: Good
Vitamin C: Excellent

Compare Potato salad made with:	4 fl oz/125 ml	
	Calories	Grams fat
mayonnaise	235	18
yogurt and sour cream	130	4

CHICKEN AND MELON SALAD

To cook whole chicken in microwave oven, put chicken in microwave dish, cover dish with greaseproof paper, folding back corner to vent steam.
Microwave on High for about 17 minutes or until juices run clear when thigh is pierced. To cook conventionally, simmer whole chicken in water to cover for 1 hour or until tender, skimming off scum occasionally.

For an elegant but easy lunch, serve this delicious main-course salad. The chicken can be cooked and all ingredients chopped a day in advance; then simply assemble the salad before serving. Instead of grapes or honeydew melon, you can substitute other melons, papaya, pineapple, mushrooms or water chestnuts.

1	small honeydew melon or canteloupe	1
1	$2\frac{1}{2}$ lb/1.25 kg chicken or 8 chicken breasts, cooked and cubed	1
4	sticks of celery, sliced	4
12 oz	seedless green or red grapes	350 g
1	small can water chestnuts, sliced (optional)	1
4 fl oz	sour cream	125 ml
4 fl oz	plain yogurt	125 ml
$1\frac{1}{2}$ tsp	curry powder	7 ml
	Salt and freshly ground pepper	

Cut melon in half and remove seeds. With melon baller, scoop out pulp (alternatively, cut into cubes). In large bowl, combine melon balls, chicken, celery, grapes, and water chestnuts (if using).

In small bowl, mix together sour cream, yogurt and curry powder; stir gently into salad. Season with salt and pepper to taste. Makes 10 servings.

Calories per serving: 237
Grams fat per serving: 6
Vitamin C and niacin: Excellent
Phosphorus: Good

MELON AND BEAN SALAD

Red kidney beans, juicy melon balls and strips of sweet red pepper are a delicious combination that will perk up any meal from cold chicken to home-made burgers and sandwiches.

1	cantaloupe or honeydew melon	1
1	can (15.2oz/432 g) red or white kidney beans, drained	1
2	spring onions (including tops)	2
1	small red pepper	1
1	garlic clove, chopped	1
2 tbsp	chopped fresh parsley	30 ml
2 tbsp	lemon juice	30 ml
2 tbsp	olive oil	30 ml
	Salt and freshly ground pepper	

Cut melon in half, scoop out seeds. With melon baller, scoop out pulp (alternatively, cut into cubes). Place melon balls in salad bowl and toss with kidney beans. Cut onions and red pepper into thin strips about 1 to $1\frac{1}{2}$ inches/2.5 to 4 cm long; add onion, peppers, garlic and parsley to melon-kidney bean mixture; toss to mix.

Whisk together lemon juice and oil; pour over salad. Add salt and pepper to taste, toss to mix. Cover and refrigerate until serving time. (Salad may be refrigerated for up to 3 days.) Makes 8 servings.

Calories per serving: 114
Grams fat per serving: 3
Fibre: Excellent
Vitamins A and C: Excellent

CRACKED WHEAT WITH PEAS AND ONIONS

Serve this as a salad or instead of a starchy vegetable such as potatoes. It's good with beef, chicken and fish. Bulgur, or cracked wheat, is available at some supermarkets and most health food stores. Sesame oil is used for flavour, but taste the dish first, and if you like it without oil, then omit it altogether.

5 oz	bulgur (cracked wheat)	150 g
12 oz	green peas (fresh or frozen)	350 g
5	spring onions, chopped	5
3 tbsp	lemon juice	45 ml
8 tbsp	chopped fresh parsley	125 ml
	Salt and freshly ground pepper	
1 tbsp	sesame oil	15 ml

Pour enough boiling water over bulgur to cover by at least 1 inch/2.5 cm; let stand for 20 to 30 minutes or until tender and doubled in volume. Drain thoroughly, pressing out excess water. Cook peas in boiling water for 1 minute; drain.

In salad bowl, combine bulgur, peas, onions, lemon juice, parsley, and salt and pepper to taste. Sprinkle with oil and toss to mix. Serve cold or at room temperature. Makes 8 servings.

Calories per serving: 125
Grams fat per serving: 2
Fibre: Excellent
Vitamin C: Excellent

WHITE KIDNEY BEAN SALAD

Cannellini or white kidney beans make a delicious salad when teamed with summer garden vegetables. Add cucumber and tomato and you have a salad with a difference. If white kidney beans are not available, use red. Serve as part of a salad plate, with hamburgers or cold chicken, or toss with spinach for a substantial salad.

1	can (15.2 oz/432 g) Cannellini or white kidney beans, drained	1
$\frac{1}{4}$	cucumber, chopped	$\frac{1}{4}$
$\frac{1}{2}$	large Spanish or sweet onion, chopped	$\frac{1}{2}$
1	sweet green pepper, chopped	1
1	large tomato, chopped	1
2 tbsp	lemon juice	30 ml
1 tbsp	olive oil	15 ml
Pinch	cumin (or more, to taste)	Pinch
	Salt and freshly ground pepper	
	Lettuce (optional)	

Rinse beans under cold water; drain. In medium bowl, combine beans, cucumber, onion, green pepper, tomato, lemon juice, oil and cumin. Taste, and add more lemon juice, cumin, and salt and pepper to suit. Cover and refrigerate until serving. Serve alone or on lettuce. Makes 6 servings.

Calories per serving: 120
Grams fat per serving: 3
Fibre: Excellent
Vitamin C: Excellent
Iron: Good

Summer Salad Plate
White Kidney Bean Salad (page 74)
Devilled eggs
Spinach greens with Creamy Herb Dressing (page 82)

White Kidney Bean Salad
Keep a can of white beans on hand for a salad you can make at a moment's notice. Toss 1 can (15.2 oz/432 g) well-drained white beans with 2 tbsp/30 ml olive oil, 2 garlic cloves, chopped, chopped fresh parsley, and salt, pepper and lemon juice to taste. Makes 4 servings.

10-minute Autumn Supper
Corn on the cob
Sliced tomatoes
White Kidney Bean Salad (page 74)
Wholewheat bread
Fresh blackberries or peaches
Milk

SPINACH SUPPER SALAD

*Alfalfa sprouts are available from many supermarkets and health food shops but you could substitute beansprouts if they are hard to find.

On a hot summer night, this is a perfect light meal with French bread, cold soup and, for dessert, fresh fruit. This salad is also delicious with Oil and Vinegar Dressing (page 83).

4 oz	spinach leaves, torn	125 g
$\frac{1}{2}$	head leaf lettuce, in bite-size pieces	$\frac{1}{2}$
2 oz	alfalfa sprouts*	50 g
4 oz	mushrooms, sliced	125 g
1	large tomato, cut in chunks	1
2	spring onions, chopped	2
2 oz	feta cheese, crumbled	50 g
1	hard-boiled egg, coarsely chopped	1
4 tbsp	Creamy Herb Dressing (page 82, $\frac{1}{4}$ recipe)	60 ml

In large shallow salad bowl, toss spinach, lettuce and alfalfa sprouts, or arrange on individual salad plates. Sprinkle mushrooms, tomato, green onions, feta cheese and egg over top. Drizzle dressing over all. Makes 2 main-course or 6 side-salad servings.

Main-course serving	Without Dressing	With Creamy Herb Dressing
Calories per serving:	232	250
Grams fat per serving:	10.3	12

Fibre: Excellent
Calcium, phosphorus, iron, vitamins A and C, riboflavin, niacin and thiamin: Excellent

Side-salad-size serving	Oil and Vinegar Herb Dressing	Creamy Herb Dressing
Calories per serving:	92	83
Grams fat per serving:	5.6	4

MEDITERRANEAN LENTIL SALAD

Brown lentils instead of red are better for salads. They retain their shape after cooking and are tender but not mushy. This salad keeps well in the refrigerator and is delicious served on salad plates with sliced tomatoes, artichoke hearts, green beans or asparagus in a vinaigrette.

6 oz	brown lentils	175 g
6 oz	carrots, diced	175 g
1	large red onion, diced	1
2	large garlic cloves, chopped	2
1	bay leaf	1
½ tsp	dried thyme	2 ml
2 tbsp	olive oil	30 ml
2 tbsp	lemon juice	30 ml
1	celery stick, diced	1
4 tbsp	chopped fresh parsley	60 ml
1 tsp	salt	5 ml
¼ tsp	freshly ground pepper	1 ml

In saucepan, combine lentils, carrots, onion, garlic, bay leaf and thyme. Add enough water to cover by at least 1 inch/2.5 cm. Bring to a boil; reduce heat and simmer, uncovered, until lentils are tender but not mushy, 15 to 20 minutes. Drain and remove bay leaf. Add oil, lemon juice, celery, parsley, salt and pepper; toss to mix. Serve at room temperature. Makes 8 servings.

Calories per serving: 100
Grams fat per serving: 3
Fibre: Good
Vitamins A and C: Good

GREEK SALAD

This salad is wonderful made with home-grown sun-ripened tomatoes that haven't seen the inside of a refrigerator. Serve with soup or an omelette or as part of a salad plate.

3	large ripe tomatoes, chopped	3
2	cucumbers, peeled, and chopped	2
1	small red onion or 2 spring onions, chopped (optional)	1
4 tbsp	olive oil	60 ml
4 tsp	lemon juice	20 ml
1½ tsp	dried oregano	7 ml
	Salt and freshly ground pepper	
4 oz	feta cheese, crumbled	125 g
6	black olives (preferably Greek) sliced	6

In shallow salad bowl or on serving platter, combine tomatoes, cucumber and onion. Sprinkle with oil, then with lemon juice, oregano, and salt and pepper to taste. Sprinkle feta cheese and olives over salad. Makes 6 servings.

Calories per serving: 126
Grams fat per serving: 9
Vitamin C: Excellent
Vitamin A, calcium and riboflavin: Good

CHICK PEA SALAD WITH RED ONION AND TOMATO

Chick peas, or garbanzo beans, are popular in the south of France and make a delicious substantial salad. Serve as part of a salad plate with a green salad and dark bread for a light yet high-fibre lunch or supper. It's ideal as part of a meatless meal—chick peas are high in protein as well as in fibre and iron.

1	can (15.2 oz/432 g) chick peas, drained	1
$\frac{1}{2}$	red onion or 2 spring onions, finely chopped	$\frac{1}{2}$
2	garlic cloves, chopped	2
1	tomato, diced	1
8 tbsp	chopped fresh parsley	125 ml
3 tbsp	olive oil	45 ml
1 tbsp	lemon juice	15 ml
	Salt and freshly ground pepper	

In salad bowl, combine all ingredients and toss. Chill for 2 hours to blend and develop flavours before serving. Taste and adjust seasoning. Makes 4 servings.

Calories per serving: 361
Grams fat per serving: 14
Fibre: Excellent
Vitamin C and iron: Excellent
Vitamin A, niacin, thiamin and phosphorus: Good

BERMUDA BEAN SALAD

This salad is good with just about any meal, especially home-made beefburgers. It keeps well in the refrigerator, and is handy at a picnic or a party for entertaining a crowd. The recipe can easily be halved but make the same amount of marinade.

1 lb	fresh green beans	450 g

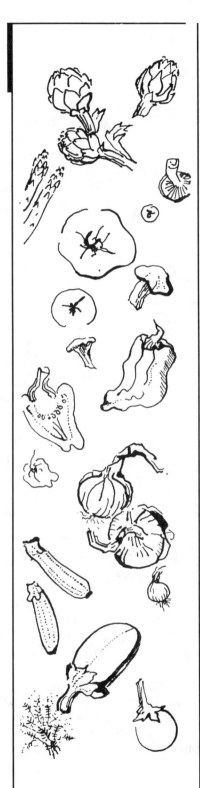

1	can (15.2 oz/432 g) red kidney beans, drained	1
1	can (15.2 oz/432 g) lima or broad beans, drained	1
1	can (15.2 oz/432 g) chick peas, drained	1
1	can (15.2 oz/432 g) white kidney beans (cannellini), drained	1
2	sweet green peppers, chopped	2
½	sweet red onion, thinly sliced	½

Marinade

4 fl oz	red wine vinegar	125 ml
4 tbsp	vegetable oil	60 ml
5 tbsp	granulated sugar	75 ml
5 tbsp	packed brown sugar	75 ml
1 tsp	freshly ground pepper	5 ml
½ tsp	salt	2 ml

Snap ends off fresh beans and cut into 1½ inch/4 cm pieces. Cook beans in rapidly boiling water for 3 minutes; plunge into cold water until cool, then drain and pat dry. In large bowl, combine cooked beans, kidney beans, broad beans, chick peas, green peppers and onions.

Marinade: Combine vinegar, oil, both sugars, pepper and salt; stir until sugar dissolves and pour over bean mixture. Marinate in refrigerator overnight. Makes 20 servings.

Calories per serving: 248
Grams fat per serving: 4
Fibre: Excellent
Vitamin C: Excellent
Iron, thiamin, niacin and phosphorus: Good

PASTA SALAD WITH SWEET PEPPERS AND DILL

*If fresh dill isn't available, substitute fresh parsley and 1 tsp/5 ml each dried dillweed and either basil or oregano.

You can add any of the usual salad ingredients to this dish except lettuce. It's a terrific salad to have in the refrigerator for a quick and easy summer meal or a picnic. Vegetables can be crisply cooked, but I like the crunch of them raw. To serve as a main course, add julienne strips of ham, chicken and/or cheese.

8 oz	flat egg noodles or fusilli	225 g
4 oz	mangetout or green beans	125 g
$\frac{1}{2}$	cauliflower, in small pieces	$\frac{1}{2}$
6 oz	carrots, thinly sliced	175 g
2	sweet peppers (red, yellow, green, or combination), chopped	2
2	spring onions, chopped	2
4 tbsp	chopped fresh dill*	60 ml
Dressing		
2	garlic cloves, chopped	2
5 tbsp	red wine vinegar	75 ml
1 tbsp	granulated sugar	15 ml
5 tbsp	corn oil	75 ml
3 tbsp	water	45 ml
	Salt and freshly ground pepper	

In large saucepan of boiling water, cook pasta until al dente (tender but firm—start tasting after 2 minutes for fresh pasta, 5 minutes for dry); drain, rinse under cold running water and drain again.

Blanch mangetout or green beans in boiling water for 2 minutes. Drain; rinse under cold running water and drain again. Cut diagonally into 2 inch/5 cm lengths.

In large bowl, combine cauliflower, carrots, peppers, spring onions, dill, mangetout and pasta; toss to mix.

Dressing: In food processor or bowl, combine garlic, vinegar and sugar; mix well. While whisking or processing, gradually add oil and water; mix well. Pour over salad and toss to mix. Add salt and pepper to taste. Makes about 10 servings.

Lunch Menus for Entertaining:
Spring
Chicken and Melon Salad
(page 71)
Tossed green salad
Asparagus with Orange
Vinaigrette (page 84)
Old-Fashioned Molasses Bread
(page 180)
Lemon Charlotte with
Strawberries (page 202)

Summer
Pasta Salad with Sweet Peppers
and Dill (page 80)
Sliced tomatoes with basil
Wholewheat Raisin Scones
(page 182)
Peaches with Raspberry Coulis
(page 193)

Autumn
Seafood Chowder (page 48)
Artichoke and Tomato Salad
(page 63)
Wholewheat Irish Soda Bread
(page 181)
Apple Cinnamon Sorbet
(page 194)
Almond Meringues (page 179)

Winter
Tex-Mex Chilli (page 104) or
Fettuccine with Clam Sauce
(page 108)
Wholewheat toast
Broccoli Buffet Salad (page 62)
or Spinach and Red Cabbage
Salad (page 61)
Apple Sauce Wholewheat Cake
(page 215)
Grapefruit Ice (page 196)

Calories per serving: 288
Grams fat per serving: 7.7
Vitamins A and C and thiamin: Excellent
Iron and niacin: Good
Fibre: Good, when made with wholewheat pasta
(otherwise fair)

SALAD DRESSINGS

Beware of salad dressings: when made with mayonnaise, cream or oil, they can add a wicked amount of fat to your diet. You can make delicious dressings with low-fat yogurt or semi-skimmed milk, and just a touch of oil, with fresh herbs, mustard or garlic for added flavour.

To reduce the fat in your usual recipes, substitute plain low-fat yogurt or semi-skimmed milk for half of the mayonnaise or sour cream you usually use. You'll be surprised at the results—the dressing will be lighter and have added flavour.

Try some of our dressings—most of them are very low in fat compared to traditional recipes for dressings. If buying commercial varieties, choose the calorie-reduced kind.

Diet Hint: Reducing fat content of salad dressings
1. Instead of using mayonnaise, sour cream or whipping cream in creamy dressings, substitute half or more of the quantity called for with yogurt, semi-skimmed milk or cottage cheese and process in blender or food processor for a smooth texture.
2. Instead of using all the oil called for in an oil and vinegar dressing, use half the amount and make up the difference with water, orange juice, tomato juice or beef stock (if the vinegar flavour is too strong, add a little sugar).
3. Use only enough dressing to lightly coat the salad ingredients. Don't let them drown!
4. Nuts are deceptively high in fat, although they are an excellent source of fibre. When the rest of the menu is high in fat, substitute water chestnuts for nuts in salad to achieve a crunchy texture.

CREAMY HERB DRESSING

8 fl oz	plain yogurt	250 ml
4 fl oz	low-fat mayonnaise	125 ml
2 tbsp	lemon juice	30 ml
1½ tsp	dried dillweed or 5 tbsp/75 ml chopped fresh dill	7 ml
1 tsp	Dijon mustard	5 ml
½ tsp	salt	2 ml
1	garlic clove, chopped	1
	Freshly ground pepper	
5 tbsp	chopped fresh parsley	75 ml

In mixing bowl or large measuring cup, combine all ingredients. Using whisk or fork, mix well. Cover and refrigerate for up to 1 week. Makes 13 fl oz/400 ml.

Calories per 1 tbsp/15 ml: 21
Grams fat per 1 tbsp/15 ml: 1.6

OIL AND VINEGAR DRESSING

Variation
Herb Vinaigrette: Add $\frac{1}{4}$ tsp/1 ml each crumbled dried thyme leaves and celery seed, and 1 tbsp/15 ml chopped fresh herbs or parsley.

A classic oil and vinegar dressing uses 3 parts oil to 1 part vinegar (e.g., 6 fl oz/175 ml oil and 2 fl oz/60 ml vinegar), and has about 10 grams fat per 1 tbsp/15 ml. To reduce the fat content, replace half the oil with water, orange juice, or beef or chicken stock, and add a pinch of sugar.

Use this delicious dressing on green salads, pasta salads, as a marinade for vegetables, or with any salad for which you want a vinaigrette dressing. It has about half the fat content of a home-made oil and vinegar dressing, but use it sparingly—it is still high in fat.

2 tbsp	vinegar	30 ml
$\frac{1}{2}$ tsp	Dijon mustard	2 ml
1	garlic clove, chopped (optional)	1
	Salt and freshly ground pepper	
4 tbsp	olive oil	60 ml
3 tbsp	water	45 ml
$\frac{1}{2}$ tsp	granulated sugar (optional)	2 ml

In small bowl or food processor, combine vinegar, mustard, garlic (if using), and salt and pepper to taste, and mix well. While whisking or processing, gradually add oil. Add water; taste, and add sugar if desired. Makes about 4 fl oz/125 ml.

Calories per 1 tbsp/15 ml: 51
Grams fat per 1 tbsp/15 ml: 6

Compare

Salad Dressings	Per 1 tbsp/15 ml	
	Grams fat our recipe	Grams fat conventional recipe
Blue Cheese	0.8	8
Creamy Herb Dressing	1.6	6
Oil and Vinegar	6	10
Orange Vinaigrette	2.8	—
Parsley Dressing	0.5	—
Tomato French	1.4	6
Yogurt and Basil	0.1	—
Thousand Island		8
Mayonnaise		11
Half mayonnaise, half plain low-fat yogurt	6	—

ORANGE VINAIGRETTE

Use this tangy oil and vinegar dressing with tossed salads or as a marinade for vegetables.

1	garlic clove	1
2 tbsp	chopped fresh parsley	30 ml
2 tbsp	white wine vinegar	30 ml
1 tsp	granulated sugar	5 ml
½ tsp	salt	2 ml
	Freshly ground pepper	
4 tbsp	orange juice	60 ml
2 tbsp	vegetable oil	30 ml

In food processor or blender; chop garlic and parsley. Add vinegar, sugar, salt, and pepper to taste; process to mix. With motor running, gradually add orange juice and oil. Makes about 4 fl oz/125 ml.

Calories per 1 tbsp/15 ml: 32
Grams fat per 1 bsp/15 ml: 2.8

BLUE CHEESE DRESSING

Using yogurt instead of traditional mayonnaise in this dressing makes a lighter but equally good-tasting dressing that's much lower in both fat and calories. Use with green and spinach salads.

2½ oz	blue cheese, crumbled	75 g
8 fl oz	plain yogurt	250 ml
1	garlic clove, chopped	1
Pinch	dry mustard	Pinch
	Freshly ground pepper	

In small bowl, use a fork to cream half of the cheese. Stir in yogurt, garlic, mustard and pepper to taste; mix well. Stir in remaining cheese. Cover and store in refrigerator. Makes about 10 fl oz/325 ml.

Calories per 1 tbsp/15 ml: 16
Grams fat per 1 tbsp/15 ml: 0.8

Spring Appetizer
Enjoy tender, crisp asparagus with a touch of tangy flavour. Sprinkle 4 fl oz/125 ml Orange Vinaigrette over 1¼ lb/575 g cooked asparagus. Makes 4 servings.

PARSLEY DRESSING

This thick, creamy dressing is one of my favourites. It's good with spinach and green salads, and can also be served as a dip for vegetables.

8 tbsp	chopped fresh parsley	125 ml
8 oz	low-fat cottage cheese	225 g
1 tsp	Dijon mustard	5 ml
1	egg	1
1 tsp	lemon juice	5 ml
	Salt and freshly ground pepper	

In food processor, chop parsley. Add cottage cheese, mustard, egg, lemon juice, and salt and pepper to taste; process until well mixed. Cover and refrigerate until needed (will keep for a few days). Makes 8 fl oz/250 ml.

Calories per 1 tbsp/15 ml: 16
Grams fat per 1 tbsp/15 ml: 0.5
Cottage cheese is a good source of calcium.

Variation
Watercress Dressing: Substitute watercress leaves (stems removed because they have too strong a flavour, and also won't chop finely in food processor) for the parsley.

YOGURT AND BASIL DRESSING

Use this low-fat dressing with green salads, cooked vegetable and pasta salads.

4 tbsp	plain yogurt	60 ml
4 tbsp	cottage cheese	60 ml
½ tsp	dried basil, or 1 tbsp/15 ml chopped fresh	2 ml
½ tsp	granulated sugar	2 ml
2 tsp	lemon juice	10 ml
	Salt and freshly ground pepper	

In a food processor or blender, combine all ingredients; blend until smooth. Makes about 4 fl oz/125 ml.

Calories per 1 tbsp/15 ml: 9
Grams fat per 1 tbsp/15 ml: 0.1

For other salad dressing recipes, see:
Balsamic Vinaigrette (page 66)
Creamy Dill Dressing (page 30)
Lemon Vinaigrette (page 67)
Yogurt Dressing (page 68)

TOMATO FRENCH DRESSING

This is one of the best low-calorie, low-fat vinaigrette dressings that I've tasted—keep it handy in your refrigerator.

4 fl oz	tomato juice	125 ml
1 tsp	cornflour	5 ml
1 tbsp	red wine vinegar	15 ml
1 tbsp	olive oil	15 ml
½ tsp	Dijon mustard	2 ml
1	small garlic clove, chopped	1
½ tsp	dried tarragon, thyme or basil, or chopped fresh herbs to taste	2 ml
	Salt and freshly ground pepper	

In small saucepan or microwave container, whisk together tomato juice and cornflour. Cook, stirring, over medium heat or at high until mixture comes to a boil and thickens. Boil 1 minute, stirring constantly. Remove from heat and whisk in remaining ingredients. Leave to cool. Transfer to jar with screw-top lid. Refrigerate until needed. Shake before using. Makes about 6 fl oz/150 ml.

Calories per 1 tbsp/15 ml: 16
Grams fat per 1 tbsp/15 ml: 1.4

Five Portable Lunch Menus

Wholewheat pitta bread filled
with Hummus (page 32),
Lettuce and bean sprouts
Apple
Milk

Raw vegetables (carrots, sweet
green and red peppers,
courgette, cauliflower) with Creamy
Fresh Dill Dip (page 30) or
Parsley Dressing (page 85)
Wholewheat roll
Banana
Milk

Green Bean Crunch (page 25)
or carrot sticks
Wholewheat roll with low-
fat cream cheese
Date Square (page 183)
Orange
Milk

Pitta bread filled with
Tabbouleh (page 64) or
Hummus (page 32)
Cantaloupe wedge
Milk

Chicken sandwich on whole-
wheat bread
Fresh grapes or figs
Milk

POULTRY

From coq au vin to tandoori, chicken is a mainstay of cuisines around the world. Its flavour appeals to children as well as to adults and it lends itself to a wide range of seasonings and sauces.

For the health-conscious cook, chicken has the added benefit of being a low-fat source of animal protein. To keep the fat at a minimum, remove the skin and any visible fat from chicken pieces before cooking; from whole chickens cut the skin away before eating (whole chickens take longer to cook and would dry out if skin were removed before cooking). Roast chicken with skin has 53 per cent fat calories, while roast chicken without skin has 31 per cent fat calories.

Obviously frying chicken adds to the fat intake; baking and grilling are far better cooking methods. Dark meat has considerably more fat than white meat. The larger and older the bird, the higher the fat content. When roasting chicken, place pieces or whole bird on a rack so the fat drips off and the chicken doesn't roast in it. Though turkey and chicken are both low in fat, duck and goose have a much higher fat content.

In the Chicken Dijon the skin is removed to reduce the fat content. Because of the mustard mixture and bread-crumb coating, the chicken stays moist. Use wholewheat bread crumbs if possible. They are quick to make using a food processor.

CHICKEN DIJON

Crisp and juicy, this chicken can be prepared ahead of time and served hot, or cold.

6	chicken breasts	6
	Salt and freshly ground pepper	
3 tbsp	Dijon mustard	45 ml
5 tbsp	plain yogurt	75 ml
1½ oz	fine fresh bread crumbs	40 g
1 tsp	thyme	5 ml

Remove skin from chicken. Sprinkle chicken lightly with salt and pepper. Mix mustard into yogurt. In another bowl, mix bread crumbs, thyme, a pinch of salt and pepper.

Spread each piece of chicken with mustard mixture, then roll in bread-crumb mixture. Place chicken in single layer on lightly greased baking sheet. Bake in 350°F/180°C/Gas Mark 4 oven for 45 to 50 minutes for bone-in chicken, 30 to 35 minutes for boneless, or until golden brown and meat is no longer pink. Makes 6 servings.

Opposite:
Orange and Ginger Chicken with Leeks (page 94)

Calories per serving: 190 (with skin on—241)
Grams fat per serving: 3.9 (with skin on—8.4)
Niacin: Excellent

CRISPY HERBED CHICKEN

Summer Dinner Menu
Fresh Tomato and Basil Soup
(page 42)
Chicken Dijon (page 88)
Herbed Green Beans with
Garlic (page 160)
Cracked Wheat and Basil Pilaf
(page 173)
Melon with Raspberries
(page 200)

*Herb-Seasoned Flour
In small jar with lid, combine
4 oz/125 g plain flour, 2 tsp/10 ml
each of salt, dried basil and
thyme, 1 tsp/5 ml each of dried
oregano, tarragon and paprika
and ½ tsp/2 ml pepper. Cover
and shake to mix; store at room
temperature. Makes about
5–6 oz/150 ml.

I keep a small jar of herb-seasoned flour on hand so I can
make this chicken dish quickly—it's one of my children's
favourites. To make only enough seasoned flour for one
meal, combine 2 tbsp/30 ml flour with 2 tsp/10 ml of dried
herbs, and salt and pepper.

6	chicken pieces (about 2 lb/1 kg, bone-in)	6
2 tbsp	Herb-Seasoned Flour*	30 ml
3 fl oz	(approx) warm water	75 ml

Remove skin from chicken; rinse chicken under cold
running water and pat dry with paper towels. Place chicken
in single layer in lightly greased shallow roasting pan or
baking dish. Use small sieve or spoon to sprinkle Herb-
Seasoned Flour over chicken. Pour warm water down the
side of pan, not directly over chicken.

Bake, uncovered, in 375°F/190°C/Gas Mark 5 oven for 40
to 50 minutes or until chicken is no longer pink inside,
basting occasionally with liquid in pan to brown top of
chicken. Add more water if there's not enough liquid in pan
for basting. Makes 6 servings.

Calories per serving: 200
Grams fat per serving: 3.2
Niacin: Excellent

Compare	%fat calories
Roast chicken with skin on	53
Roast chicken without skin	31

Opposite:
Navarin of Lamb
(pages 116–117)

LEMON CHICKEN SCHNITZEL

Serve this easy to make, moist and tender chicken to family and guests. You can use boneless turkey instead of chicken.

1 lb/450 g of boneless chicken will usually serve four people; since the chicken in this recipe is cut into thin slices, it looks like a lot more, and you should be able to serve five people instead of four.

1 lb	boneless skinless chicken breasts	450 g
	Juice of 1 lemon	
4 tbsp	plain flour	60 ml
½ tsp	salt	2 ml
½ tsp	thyme	2 ml
½ tsp	celery salt	2 ml
1	egg	1
1 tsp	water	5 ml
2 oz	fine dry bread crumbs	50 g

Cut chicken horizontally into ¼ inch/5 mm thick slices. Place between 2 pieces of greaseproof paper and flatten chicken, using a rolling pin or bottom of bottle. Sprinkle chicken with lemon juice; let stand for 10 minutes.

In shallow dish, combine flour, salt, thyme and celery salt; mix well. In another shallow dish, lightly beat egg with water. Dip chicken pieces into flour mixture, then into egg mixture, then into bread crumbs. Place on lightly greased baking sheet or in microwave dish. Bake in 400°F/200°C/Gas Mark 6 oven for 10 to 15 minutes, or microwave, uncovered, on High for 4 minutes, or until chicken is no longer pink. Makes 5 servings.

Calories per serving: 180
Grams fat per serving: 5.5
Niacin: Excellent
Iron: Good

SAUTÉED CHICKEN WITH YOGURT AND MUSHROOMS

A great dish for company or guests; serve with grilled tomatoes, a green vegetable and rice. Any kind of mushrooms can be used—domestic, wild or dried (soak dried mushrooms for about 30 minutes). Try shiitake, cep, oyster, or a combination.

6	chicken pieces (about 2 lb/1 kg bone-in)	6
1 tbsp	plain flour	15 ml
1 oz	butter	25 g
2	onions, thinly sliced	2
4 oz	mushrooms, sliced	125 g
4 fl oz	water (or half water and half white wine)	125 ml
4 fl oz	plain yogurt	125 ml
	Salt and freshly ground pepper	

Remove skin from chicken. Sprinkle chicken lightly with flour. In large nonstick frying pan, melt butter over medium-high heat; cook chicken until browned all over, about 5 minutes on each side. Reduce heat to medium or medium-low and cook for 10 minutes longer on each side or until meat is no longer pink. Remove from pan and keep warm.

Add onions and mushrooms to pan and cook, stirring often, until tender, 5 to 10 minutes. Stir in water and bring to a full boil, loosening any brown bits on bottom of pan to flavour sauce. Remove from heat and stir in yogurt, and salt and pepper to taste. Return chicken to pan and spoon sauce over it. Makes 6 servings.

Calories per serving: 200
Grams fat per serving: 6
Niacin: Excellent
Calcium, phosphorus and riboflavin: Good

BREAST OF CHICKEN FLORENTINE

This recipe may look lengthy but it isn't hard to make. Because most of the preparation can be done in advance, it's ideal for a dinner party. It takes only minutes to cook, so complete the dish just before serving while you reheat the sauce and spinach. Serve with Two-Cabbage Stir-Fry (page 159) or grilled tomato halves and brown rice.

4 tbsp	plain flour	60 ml
½ tsp	salt	2 ml
½ tsp	thyme	2 ml
	Pepper to taste	
1	egg, lightly beaten	1
1 tbsp	water	15 ml
2 oz	fine dry bread crumbs	50 g
4 tbsp	grated Parmesan cheese	60 ml
4	boneless skinless chicken breasts (about 1 lb/450 g)	4
	Tarragon and Mushroom Sauce (page 150)	
1 lb	spinach	450 g
1 tsp	fresh lemon juice	5 ml
1 tsp	butter	5 ml
	Salt and freshly ground pepper	

On plate, combine flour, salt, thyme, and pepper to taste; mix well. In shallow bowl, combine egg and water; mix well. On another plate, combine bread crumbs and cheese. Coat chicken pieces with seasoned flour; shake off excess. Dip into beaten-egg mixture, then roll in cheese-crumb mixture. Refrigerate for 20 minutes or up to 2 hours.

Prepare Tarragon and Mushroom Sauce, if desired.

On lightly greased baking sheet or microwave dish, bake chicken in 400°F/200°C/Gas Mark 6 oven for 15 minutes, or microwave, uncovered, on High for 4 to 5 minutes, or until chicken is no longer pink. If microwaving, let stand for 1 to 2 minutes (cooking time will vary, depending on thickness of chicken).

Trim stems from spinach. Wash and place in saucepan with just the water clinging to leaves. Cover and cook over medium-high heat until spinach has wilted.

Drain thoroughly, and chop coarsely; toss with lemon juice, butter, and salt and pepper to taste. Place on warm dinner plates or platter to keep warm in 200°F/100°C/Gas Mark ¼ oven until chicken is cooked.

Place chicken on top of spinach and garnish with a few spoonfuls of Tarragon and Mushroom Sauce. Makes 4 servings.

Calories per serving: 260
Grams fat per serving: 6.2
Fibre: Excellent
Vitamins A and C and niacin: Excellent
Iron and phosphorus: Good
Spinach is an excellent source of fibre.

Compare	Per 3½ oz/100 g Grams fat
Kentucky-fried chicken (1 piece)	17
Grilled breast of chicken without skin (1 piece)	4

ORANGE AND GINGER CHICKEN WITH LEEKS

Chinese rice vermicelli, or rice sticks, are available in some supermarkets and Chinese grocery stores. They take only a few minutes to boil or, for a special occasion, drop a few noodles at a time into hot oil in a wok and watch them explode to six times their volume.

A quickly prepared dish for guests or family. To make it special, garnish with slices of fresh mango or grapes and cooked mangetout. Serve over Chinese vermicelli.

1¼ lb	boneless skinless chicken breasts	575 g
2	large leeks	2
1 tbsp	butter	15 ml
2	spring onions, chopped	2
4 tbsp	dry white wine	60 ml
1 tbsp	grated fresh ginger root	15 ml
1	tomato, peeled, seeded and chopped	1
4 fl oz	fresh orange juice	125 ml
½ tsp	grated orange rind	2 ml
1 tbsp	plain flour	15 ml
¼ tsp	granulated sugar	1 ml
6 oz	seedless green grapes	175 g
	Salt and freshly ground pepper	

Cut chicken into 1 inch/2.5 cm cubes. Cut off and discard tough green part of leeks. Cut leeks in half and wash thoroughly under cold water. Cut into matchstick size julienne strips.

In large, heavy frying pan, melt butter. Cook chicken over high heat, for 2 to 3 minutes or until lightly browned; remove chicken to side plate. Stir in leeks and onions and cook 1 minute, or until leeks are wilted. Stir in wine, ginger and tomato, scraping up any brown bits from bottom of pan.

In a bowl, combine orange juice, rind, flour and sugar; mix until smooth. Pour into hot mixture, stirring constantly. Bring to a boil, stirring constantly, and simmer 2 to 3 minutes. (Dish may be prepared in advance to this point. Reheat sauce.) Return chicken to pan. Stir in grapes, and salt and pepper to taste. Makes 4 servings.

Calories per serving: 337
Grams fat per serving: 13
Vitamin C, niacin and phosphorus: Excellent
Iron: Good

Stir-frying

Stir-frying is a quick and easy way to cook meats, poultry, seafood and vegetables. By frying in a small amount of oil over high heat and stirring continuously and vigorously, foods are seared and quickly cooked. Vegetables are crisp, and meats are very tender. You can control the temperature by moving the pan on and off the heat.

Use a wok or heavy frying pan. Heat the oil before adding the ingredients; otherwise, the food will absorb the oil.

Because stir-frying is so fast, have all your food chopped and measured before you start to cook. The food should be evenly shredded, diced or cut into thin slices so it will cook in a short time. By cutting meats and vegetables on the diagonal, meats will be tenderized, and the largest possible surface area of the food is exposed to the heat.

To add flavour and tenderize the meat, marinate it in advance; using cornflour in the marinade helps to tenderize the meat and thicken the dish.

When using vegetables that require a longer cooking time, add a little water, chicken stock or rice vinegar, then cover and steam for a few minutes. When preparing a large quantity of stir-fried vegetables, blanch the longer-cooking vegetables first (blanch cut vegetables in boiling water, then cool under cold running water, to prevent further cooking).

*To toast almonds, roast on a baking tray in 350°F/180°C/Gas Mark 4 oven for 5 minutes or until golden.

FOUR-MINUTE CHICKEN

Stir-frying is a great way to make one pound of chicken serve four people and look like a lot. It's a great family dish that's pretty enough for casual entertaining. Serve over rice or noodles.

4 tsp	cornflour	20 ml
2 tbsp	low-sodium soy sauce	30 ml
1 lb	boneless skinless chicken breast, cut into strips	450 g
4 fl oz	chicken stock	125 ml
2 tbsp	vegetable oil	30 ml
4	celery sticks, thinly sliced	4
8 oz	green beans or mangetout, diagonally cut	225 g
6 oz	carrots, thinly sliced carrots	175 g
1	large onion, halved and thinly sliced	1
2	garlic cloves, chopped	2
2 tbsp	water	30 ml
	Salt and freshly ground pepper	
2 tbsp	toasted sliced almonds*	30 ml

In medium bowl, combine 3 tsp/15 ml of cornflour and soy sauce; mix well. Add chicken and toss to coat; set aside. Stir remaining 1 tsp/5 ml cornflour into chicken stock; set aside.

Heat wok or heavy frying pan over medium-high heat. When hot, add oil, then chicken, and stir-fry for 4 minutes or until chicken is opaque. Remove chicken and set aside. To wok, add celery, beans, carrots, onion and garlic; stir-fry for 1 minute. Add water, cover and cook for 2 minutes. Stir chicken stock mixture into pan. Return chicken to pan; cook, stirring, for another minute or until mixture boils and vegetables are tender-crisp. Season with salt and pepper to taste. Sprinkle with toasted almonds. Makes 4 servings.

Calories per serving: 340
Grams fat per serving: 13.7
Fibre: Excellent
Niacin and vitamin A: Excellent
Iron: Good

Step-by-Step Stir-Frying

1. Have all ingredients cut and measured.
2. Heat wok or heavy frying pan over high heat.
3. Add corn or salad oil and when hot (but not smoking), add foods in the order listed in the recipe (or the ones requiring the longest cooking time first).
4. Use a long-handled spatula or wooden spoon to continuously stir the foods.
5. Add chopped garlic, ginger or onions along with vegetables; soy sauce, sherry or vinegar at the end for flavour.
6. Mix 1 to 2 tsp/5 to 10 ml cornflour with 3 tbsp/45 ml cold water or stock and add to work to thicken dish if desired.

Once you have tried a few recipes for stir-frying, you'll find it easy to improvise and make up your own. I make a stir-fried dish for dinner at least once a week, rarely following a recipe. This lets me use up all the small quantities of raw vegetables hiding in the back of the refrigerator. Stir-frying is an excellent way to stretch a small amount of meat, chicken or seafood; and, along with the vegetables, stir-fries are ideal for low-fat main dishes.

*Soy sauce is very high in sodium. If possible, use a sodium-reduced soy sauce. If unavailable, look for naturally brewed soy sauce. The highest amount of sodium is found in chemically brewed soy sauce.

If you can't find a low-sodium soy sauce use half the amount of soy sauce and make up the other half with water.

Keep this stir-fried dish in mind for when you want a special meal but have only a few minutes to prepare it.

1 lb	boneless chicken breasts	450 g
3 tbsp	dry sherry	45 ml
4 tsp	cornflour	20 ml
2 tbsp	low-sodium soy sauce*	30 ml
1 tsp	granulated sugar	5 ml
2 tbsp	vegetable oil	30 ml
2 tsp	peeled and grated ginger root, or ¾ tsp/4 ml dried ginger	10 ml
2	onions, coarsely chopped	2
8 oz	mangetout	225 g
4 fl oz	water	125 ml

Remove skin from chicken. Cut chicken into 1 inch/2.5 cm cubes. In bowl, combine 2 tbsp/30 ml of the sherry and 3 tsp/15 ml of the cornflour; mix well. Stir in chicken. Cover, and marinate in refrigerator for at least 1 hour.

In small bowl, combine soy sauce, remaining sherry, remaining cornflour and sugar; set aside.

In large heavy frying pan or wok, heat oil over high heat until hot but not smoking. Add chicken and stir-fry for 2 minutes. Remove chicken from pan and set aside.

Add garlic and ginger to pan; stir well, then add onions, mangetout and water. Stir-fry for 2 minutes. Return chicken and soy-sauce mixture to pan and stir rapidly over high heat until hot. Serve with rice or noodles. Makes 4 servings.

Calories per serving: 307
Grams fat per serving: 13
Fibre: Good
Niacin: Excellent
Iron and Vitamin C: Good

MICROWAVE TARRAGON CHICKEN WITH JULIENNE VEGETABLES AND YOGURT HOLLANDAISE

How to Microwave Whole Poultry

Microwaving is an easy, quick and moist way to cook chicken or turkey, especially when you want to remove the meat from the bone to use in salads, such as Chicken and Melon (page 71), or other dishes such as Casserole of Turkey with Melon and Curry Sauce (page 98).

- Tie wings and legs tightly to body.
- Place bird in shallow microwave dish; cover with greaseproof paper, folding back one corner to allow steam to escape.
- Microwave chicken on High for about 17 minutes for a 2½ lb/1.2 kg chicken (6 to 7 minutes per pound/450 g), turning dish occasionally depending on your microwave.
- For 12 lb/6 kg turkey, microwave breast-side down, covered loosely with greaseproof paper, on Medium-High for 24 minutes, draining liquid once or twice. Turn breast-side up and microwave on Medium-High for ¾ to 1 hour or until meat registers 190°F/90°C (older ovens may take a longer time). Drain off juices every 15 minutes.
- Pour juices from chicken into container and refrigerate or freeze—fat will rise to the surface and solidify; lift fat off and discard. Use remaining liquid for stock or for making sauces or soups.
- Let chicken stand for 10 to 15 minutes, turkey for 20 minutes, before using.

Leeks are particulary good when cooked in this way with chicken, but carrots, courgettes or celery, or a combination of these, also work well. The sauce adds a rich flavour, yet it is deceptively low in fat and calories.

1 lb	julienned carrots, leeks, celery or courgettes	450 g
4	chicken breasts	4
	Salt and freshly ground pepper	
½ oz	butter	15 g
¼ tsp	dried tarragon or 4 sprigs fresh tarragon or rosemary	1 ml
4 fl oz	Yogurt Hollandaise (pages 150–1)	125 ml

In baking dish just large enough to hold chicken in a single layer, sprinkle half the vegetables. Remove skin from chicken. Place chicken on top of vegetables and season lightly with salt and pepper. Top with remaining vegetables and dot with butter. Sprinkle with tarragon, and salt and pepper to taste.

Cover dish with greaseproof allowing for a little steam to escape; microwave on High for 6 minutes if boneless, 8 to 10 minutes bone-in, or until chicken is no longer pink. Spoon Yogurt Hollandaise over and serve.

	Without Sauce	With Sauce
Calories per serving:	194	228
Grams fat per serving:	5.2	7

Fibre: Good
Niacin and vitamin A: Excellent
Vitamin C and phosphorus: Good

CASEROLE OF TURKEY WITH MELON AND CURRY SAUCE

Melons, mangoes or peaches add a festive touch and juicyness to this curry dish. The sauce is also good with prawn or hard-boiled eggs. If using the sauce for prawn, use half chicken stock and half clam juice.

18 oz	chopped cooked turkey (in large chunks)*	500 g
8 oz	melon balls, sliced mango or sliced peaches	225 g
Curry Sauce		
2 oz	butter	50 g
1	onion, chopped	1
1	garlic clove, minced	1
4 tsp	curry powder	20 ml
$\frac{1}{2}$ tsp	chilli powder	2 ml
$\frac{1}{2}$ tsp	cumin	2 ml
5 tbsp	plain flour	75 ml
16 fl oz	chicken stock	500 ml
$\frac{1}{2}$ tsp	salt	2 ml
	Freshly ground pepper	

Curry Sauce: In flameproof casserole or saucepan, melt butter. Stir in onion, garlic, curry powder, chilli powder and cumin; cook, stirring, over medium-low heat until onion is tender. Stir in flour and mix well. Stir in stock; bring to a boil, stirring, and simmer, uncovered, for 5 minutes. Add salt and pepper to taste.

Stir in turkey. (Casserole may be prepared in advance to this point, covered, and refrigerated for up to 2 days. Reheat gently before continuing with recipe). Add melon, or other fruit and cook, stirring, until heated through, 5 to 10 minutes. Makes 6 servings.

Calories per serving: 209
Grams fat per serving: 7
Iron, niacin and vitamin C: Excellent
Phosphorus: Good
Cantaloupe melon is an excellent source of vitamin A and a good source of vitamin C.

Boxing Day Buffet
Casserole of Turkey with Melon and Curry Sauce
(page 98)
Brown and wild rice
Chutney
Steamed mangetout
Tossed green salad
French bread
Orange Sponge Cake
(page 213) with Sherry Orange Sauce (page 201) and Frozen Lemon Cream (page 195)

This is a lovely buffet casserole. It's easy to eat without a knife and can be prepared in advance. (Add melon just before serving.) It can be easily doubled or tripled for a larger number of guests. You can substitute chicken for the turkey and can also include prawns. Plan on about $\frac{1}{4}$ lb/125 g mangetout per person or use less and serve another vegetable as well.

Hard-Boiled Eggs with Curry Sauce
Here's a delicious dish at an Easter buffet. In a large frying pan, prepare Curry Sauce (page 171). Add peeled, halved hard-boiled eggs (about $1\frac{1}{2}$ eggs per person) to Curry Sauce and warm over low heat until heated through, about 5 minutes. Serve over rice.

*You can substitute chicken for the turkey. See page 97 for microwave instructions.

To Roast Turkey or Chicken

- Truss bird, with string, tying wings and legs close to body (do not use synthetic string).
- Place bird on rack in roasting pan. This makes it easier to remove the bird and keeps it from cooking in its own juices and fat.
- Cover turkey lightly with lid or foil (shiny side down); remove foil during last hour of roasting to brown top.
- Bird is cooked when it reaches an internal temperature of 185°F/90°C, drumstick moves easily in socket and juices from thigh run clear when pierced.
- Remove from oven and transfer to platter; let stand for 15 minutes before carving.
- Roast turkey in 325°F/160°C/ Gas Mark 3 oven for 4 to 5 hours for 12 to 14 lb/5.5 to 6.5 kg bird (20 to 25 minutes per pound/450 g if small; 15 minutes per pound/450 g if over 18 lb/8 kg).

- Roast chicken in 350°F/180°C/Gas Mark 4 oven for about 1½ hours for 4 lb/2 kg chicken.

Diet Hint: Reducing fat content when roasting chicken or turkey

- Avoid recipes for stuffing that use oil or butter.
- Instead of stuffing poultry, slip garlic slivers, fresh herbs, sliced fresh ginger root under the skin (between flesh and skin) or place in cavity.
- Stuff cavity with apple slices, onion wedges, mushrooms and/or orange sections.
- If making a bread stuffing, use fairly fresh bread, or moisten stale bread with chicken stock; add chopped onions, celery and apple instead of oil or butter.
- Instead of gravy, serve pan juices with fat removed, Bramble Sauce (page 147) or cranberry sauce (you can add flavour and interest with chutney, port or brandy).
- Discard skin before serving.

MEAT

Meat can be a high source of fat in our diet. One way of reducing our intake of fat is to eat lean cuts of meat, and to cut down on the amount of meat we eat. Remember: Cut down, DON'T *cut out*. Meat is an important source of complete protein; this means it has all the essential amino acids, the building blocks of protein. Meat is also an important source of iron in a form the body can easily use, as well as a good source of B vitamins and minerals. Just 3½ ounces/100 g of cooked lean beef (such as steak or lean hamburger) provides 25 g of protein and nearly 3 mg of iron. This constitutes more than half of an adult's estimated average daily requirement for protein and almost one third of a male adult's estimated average daily requirement for iron (girls, teenagers and women 11–49 yrs require up to 15 mg of iron per day).

The problem is that we don't often limit our meat portions to 3 to 4 ounces/90 to 125 g. We eat fatty marbled as well as lean meat. To help us eat more healthily, the meat industry is producing leaner beef and pork.

To keep the size of portions down, yet still make them appear satisfying, use meat in mixed dishes such as stir-fries, stews and soups, or in sauces such as spaghetti sauce. As a nation, we still aren't used to eating only 4 ounce/125 g portions of steak, but if you slice the steak in thin slices before serving, a 4 ounce/125 g portion will look like much more.

BEEF AND VEGETABLE STEW

Stews are an ideal way to serve a 4 oz/125 g portion of meat without appearing skimpy. With the addition of vegetables, this not only stretches the meat but increases the fibre; add a potato (boiled with skin) per person and the fibre content is as much as 5 g per serving.

When making any kind of stew, make it a day in advance and refrigerate. Any fat will solidify on the surface and then can easily be removed.

This savoury stew tastes even better the second day when flavours have had a chance to blend. Serve with mashed or boiled potatoes or over hot noodles.

1¼ lb	stewing beef	575 g
2 tbsp	plain flour	30 ml
1 tbsp	vegetable oil	15 ml
16 fl oz	water	500 ml
3	onions, quartered	3
1	bay leaf	1
1 tsp	thyme	5 ml
½ tsp	marjoram or oregano	2 ml
1 tsp	salt	5 ml

- Buy lean cuts of meat such as flank, sirloin and lean minced beef.
- Trim all visible fat from meat.
- When browning meat or cooking minced meat, pour off all fat before adding other ingredients.
- Cook stews and simmered meat dishes a day in advance and refrigerate overnight. The next day you can easily remove hardened fat from the surface.
- Cut off any fat from cooked meat before eating.
- Processed meats such as salami, hot dogs and sausages are usually high in fat as well as salt, nitrates and nitrites. They should be avoided, or eaten in only small amounts
- Most important of all, cook meat without adding extra fat. Don't fry instead grill, roast or microwave.

See Table C, pages 230–2, for fat content of various meats.

$\frac{1}{4}$ tsp	freshly ground pepper	1 ml
1 tsp	grated orange rind	5 ml
1	small turnip (about 1 lb/450 g)	1
5	carrots	5
6 oz	frozen peas	175 g
4 tbsp	chopped fresh parsley	60 ml
	Salt and freshly ground pepper	

Cut all visible fat from beef and discard. Cut beef into about 1 inch/2.5 cm cubes. Coat beef with flour, using up all flour.

In heavy pan, heat oil over medium-high heat. Add beef and cook, stirring, until brown on all sides.

Pour in water and bring to a boil, scraping up any brown bits on bottom of pan. Add onions, bay leaf, thyme, marjoram, salt, pepper and orange rind. Cover, and simmer for $1\frac{1}{2}$ hours.

Peel turnip and cut into $\frac{3}{4}$ inch/2 cm pieces. Scrape carrots and cut into 1 inch/2.5 cm pieces. Add carrots and turnip to pan; simmer, covered, for 40 minutes or until vegetables are tender. Add peas, parsley, and salt and pepper to taste. Simmer until peas are hot. Makes 6 servings.

Calories per serving: 220
Grams fat per serving: 9
Fibre: Excellent
Niacin and vitamins A and C: Excellent
Iron: Good

Making the Most of Pan Juices

Pan juices from roasting meats are flavourful and make a wonderful sauce. To remove fat, either use a large spoon and skim from surface, or add a tray of ice cubes to the juices (the fat will cool and harden, and can then be easily removed). Bring the juices to a boil; boil for a few minutes to evaporate extra water and reduce sauce to desired consistency.

Pan juices and brown bits on the bottom of the pan after grilling or sautéing meats, chicken and fish make a good base for a savoury sauce. Simply spoon off the fat, add a large spoonful or two of wine, vinegar or fruit juice and bring to a boil, scraping up all brown bits from bottom of the pan. Add other flavourings, such as garlic, onions, shallots and parsley, if desired. Remove from heat and stir in a little yogurt.

MARINATED STEAK

This is my son John's favourite steak. It's tender, and one of the leanest cuts of beef.

1 lb	flank steak	450 g
4 tbsp	soy sauce	60 ml
4 tbsp	vegetable oil	60 ml
2 tbsp	vinegar	30 ml
2 tbsp	sugar or honey	30 ml
1 tbsp	peeled and grated fresh ginger root or 1 tsp/5 ml ground ginger	15 ml

Score one side of the steak by making shallow cuts in a crisscross pattern. Place meat in a shallow dish. Combine soy sauce, oil, vinegar, sugar and ginger; pour over meat. Cover, and refrigerate for 1 to 3 days, or at room temperature for up to 3 hours.

Remove meat from marinade and grill for 4 to 5 minutes on each side. Slice thinly on an angle across the grain. Serve hot or cold. Makes 4 servings.

Calories per serving: 200
Grams fat per serving: 9
Niacin: Excellent
Iron, riboflavin and niacin: Good

STUFFED PEPPERS WITH TOMATO AND BASIL SAUCE

September Family Supper
Stuffed Peppers with
Tomato and Basil Sauce
(page 103)
Steamed carrots
Wholewheat bread
Peach Blackcurrant Crisp
(page 208)

Stuffed peppers can be frozen.
Cook frozen or thawed peppers
in a microwave or in a
conventional oven.

*Instead of tomato sauce, you
can use 4 tbsp/60 ml each
tomato purée and water
(mixed), or 8 tbsp/120 ml
ketchup.

Variation
Instead of Tomato and Basil
Sauce, sprinkle stuffed peppers
with grated Parmesan cheese or
low-fat mozzarella cheese
before baking.

Sweet peppers are now available from markets and
supermarkets all year round. So you can serve this dish
winter and summer. For a really attractive dish use peppers in
a variety of colours.

12	red, green, or yellow peppers (medium size)	12
12 oz	lean minced beef	350 g
1	onion, finely chopped	1
14 oz	cooked rice (7 oz/200 g uncooked)	400 g
12 oz	drained canned or chopped fresh tomatoes	350 g
8 tbsp	tomato sauce*	120 ml
1 tbsp	Worcestershire sauce	15 ml
1 tsp	salt	5 ml
12 fl oz	Tomato and Basil Sauce (page 149)	375 ml

Slice top off each pepper; chop tops and save to add to
filling. Remove core, seeds and white membranes from
peppers. Blanch peppers in boiling water for 3 minutes; drain
and set aside.

In large frying pan or heavy saucepan, cook beef, onion
and chopped pepper until beef is browned and onions are
tender. Drain off any fat. Stir in rice, tomatoes, tomato sauce,
Worcestershire sauce and salt; simmer for 2 minutes. Spoon
meat mixture into peppers. (Recipe may be prepared ahead
to this point and refrigerated or frozen). Bake in
350°F/180°C/Gas Mark 4 oven for 20 minutes or until hot.
Serve with Tomato and Basil Sauce to spoon over. Makes 6
servings.

Calories per serving: 213
Grams fat per serving: 6
Vitamins A and C and niacin: Excellent
Iron, riboflavin and phosphorus: Good

TEX-MEX CHILLI

*Soak red kidney beans overnight in water, drain and rinse well. Bring to the boil in fresh water and boil fast for at least 10 minutes so that the toxins on the beans are destroyed. Then simmer until the beans are tender—about another 40 minutes. Drain.

Tex-Mex is hot and spicy Mexican food adapted to a British palate. You can add baked beans or any other type of beans.

1 lb	lean minced beef	450 g
2	large onions, coarsely chopped	2
2	large garlic cloves, chopped	2
2 tbsp	(approx) chilli powder	30 ml
1 tsp	ground cumin	5 ml
½ tsp	oregano	2 ml
½ tsp	crushed red chilli peppers	2 ml
2	can (14 oz/400 g) tomatoes	2
2 lb 4 oz	cooked red kidney beans,* or 2 cans (each 15.2 oz/432 g) drained	1 kg
1 tsp	salt	5 ml
8 oz	sweetcorn (canned, frozen or fresh)	225 g

In large heavy saucepan or nonstick frying pan, cook beef for about 5 minutes or until brown. Pour off any fat. Add onions, garlic, chilli, cumin, oregano and red pepper; cook, stirring, over low heat until onions are tender (about 5 minutes). Stir in tomatoes, kidney beans and salt; bring to a boil, reduce heat and simmer for 20 minutes, or until desired consistency is reached. Add sweetcorn, and cook until sweetcorn is heated through. Makes 6 servings.

Calories per serving: 349
Grams fat per serving: 8.5
Fibre: Excellent
Iron, niacin, vitamins A and C: Excellent
Thiamin: Good

OLD-FASHIONED MEAT LOAF

Serve this traditional meat loaf with baked potatoes and a green vegetable.

1 lb	lean minced beef	450 g
1	large onion, finely chopped	1
1	slice wholewheat bread, crumbled	1
½ tsp	thyme	2 ml
½ tsp	salt	2 ml
Dash	Worcestershire sauce	Dash
	Freshly ground pepper	
8 fl oz	tomato juice	250 ml
1	egg, lightly beaten	1
1 tbsp	chopped fresh herbs—thyme, rosemary, savory, sage (optional)	15 ml

In mixing bowl, combine beef, onion, bread crumbs, thyme, salt, Worcestershire sauce, and pepper to taste. Stir in tomato juice, egg and herbs (if using); mix lightly. Turn into 9 × 5 inch/2 L loaf pan or baking dish. Bake in 350°F/180°C/Gas Mark 4 oven for 45 minutes, or until brown and firm to the touch.

Remove from oven; pour off fat. Makes 5 servings.

	Using lean minced beef	Using ordinary minced beef
Calories per serving:	186	267
Grams fat per serving:	9.5	17
Niacin: Excellent		
Iron and phosphorus: Good		

Compare

Lean minced beef usually contains less than 10% fat. Ordinary minced beef can contain roughly double the fat but no more than 25%.

Lean, or ordinary

- Use ordinary minced beef when you can pour fat from pan after browning the meat.
- Use ordinary minced beef where some fat is needed for tenderness and juicyness (hamburgers).
- Use lean minced beef when you can't pour off the fat (shepherd's pie, or stuffing for pasta), or where other fats are in same dish, so more fat is not needed for tenderness or flavour.

Be sure to pour off any fat in pan before serving meat loaf.

BEEFBURGERS AU POIVRE

Dress up peppery beefburgers with this shallot and yogurt sauce.

1 lb	lean minced beef*	450 g
2 tsp	peppercorns**	10 ml
1 tbsp	vegetable or corn oil	15 ml
1 tbsp	finely chopped shallots***	15 ml
1 tbsp	red wine vinegar	15 ml
4 tbsp	yogurt or sour cream	60 ml
1 tbsp	chopped fresh parsley	15 ml

Divide meat into 4 portions and shape into beefburgers. Put peppercorns on large piece of greaseproof paper or foil. Using bottom of heavy pan or rolling pin, crack peppercorns coarsely. Spread peppercorns out, and place burgers on top. Press burgers down; turn burgers over and sprinkle any remaining peppercorns over top. Press peppercorns so they stick to meat.

In large frying pan, heat oil over high heat. Add burgers and cook over high heat for 2 to 3 minutes or until browned; turn and cook other side for 1 to 2 minutes or until browned, and at desired degree of cooking (reduce heat if necessary to prevent burning).

Transfer burgers to warm serving plate. Pour off fat in pan; add shallots and wine vinegar and cook over medium heat, scraping up brown bits from bottom of pan. Remove from heat; add yogurt and stir to mix well. Stir in parsley. Place burgers on individual plates, then spoon sauce over them. Makes 4 servings.

Calories per serving: 244
Grams fat per serving: 13
Niacin: Excellent
Iron and phosphorus: Good

*Because there is fat in the sauce we have used lean minced beef to reduce the overall fat content of the dish. If you are making these burgers and just serving them plain you could substitute ordinary minced beef.

**Coarsely ground peppercorns can be bought in many grocers and supermarkets and can be substituted however, freshly cracked peppercorns taste better.

***If shallots are unavailable, use cooking onions.

POT-AU-FEU

This French savoury classic consists of a pot roast of beef and various vegetables slowly simmered together. The heavenly broth can be served as a soup for the first course, and the meat and vegetables as the main course. Or, the meat and vegetables can be served as the main course on one day, then any leftovers added to the broth which can be served for dinner another night. It's best to start this a day in advance and refrigerate it overnight so the fat will solidify on top for easy removal. Serve with boiled potatoes and a sauce of Horseradish mixed with yogurt.

4 lb	(approx) boneless rib, blade or sirloin roast	2 kg
3¼ pts	water	2 L
3	large carrots	3
3	large onions	3
2	small white turnips (or half a yellow swede)	2
2	celery stalks	2
1	small cabbage	1
	Salt and freshly ground pepper	

Be sure roast is securely tied. Place in large, deep saucepan or flameproof casserole and add water. Bring to a boil over medium heat; remove any scum. Simmer for 1½ hours.

Peel carrots, onions and turnips; cut into even-sized chunks, slice the celery and add with the other vegetables to the casserole. Cover, and simmer for another hour or until vegetables are nearly tender. Skim off fat or refrigerate overnight, then remove fat.

Reheat if necessary. Quarter cabbage and add to pot. Cook for 15 minutes or until tender. Season with salt and pepper to taste. Remove meat to platter; let stand for 10 minutes before carving. Keep vegetables warm, and serve broth as a first course (save a little broth to pour over meat and vegetables). Makes 10 servings.

Calories per serving (including broth): 420
Grams fat per serving: 20
Fibre: Good
Vitamins A and C, iron and niacin: Excellent

TOMATO SAUCE PROVENÇAL WITH VEAL ON PASTA

Thin strips of tender veal combine with tomatoes and Provençal seasonings of garlic and parsley in this easy dish. The small amount of veal keeps the cost within reason and the fat content down.

1 oz	butter	25 g
1	large onion, chopped	1
2 tbsp	(approx) water	30 ml
8 oz	wholewheat noodles	225 g
1	large can (28 oz/800 g) plum tomatoes, drained	1
8 oz	lean veal	225 g
4	garlic cloves, chopped	4
8 tbsp	fresh parsley, chopped	125 ml
	Salt and freshly ground pepper	

In large heavy frying pan, melt butter over medium heat; cook onion until tender. Add water to prevent onion from burning (add more if necessary).

In large pot of boiling water, cook noodles until al dente (tender but firm). (Dry wholewheat noodles require a longer cooking time than regular noodles or fresh pasta; follow package directions and taste every few minutes.)

Coarsely chop tomatoes and add to onion in frying pan. Cut veal into 2 inch/5 cm strips about $\frac{1}{4}$ inch/5 mm wide; add to frying pan and cook over medium heat, stirring occasionally, until veal is cooked (about 2 minutes). Add garlic and parsley.

Drain noodles and arrange on hot dinner plates or platter. Season sauce with salt and pepper to taste; spoon over noodles. Serve immediately. Makes 4 main-course servings, 6 appetizer servings.

Calories per main-course serving: 574
Grams fat per main-course serving: 12
Fibre: Good
Iron, vitamins A and C and niacin: Excellent
Thiamin and riboflavin: Good

Fettuccine with Clam Sauce
For a delightfully easy pasta dish, substitute 1 can (5 oz/142 g) of clams, drained, for the veal in Tomato Sauce Provençal with Veal on Pasta. Toss with hot, drained fettuccine. For 2 to 3 people, use the same basic recipe but substitute 1 can (14 oz/400 g) tomatoes for the larger can; use slightly less pasta (toss any leftover noodles with sauce and reheat the next day in a microwave or a saucepan).

MEXICAN PORK STEW

Shopping Tip
Boneless pork shoulders are sometimes featured in supermarket special offers. Cut the meat into cubes or strips, discarding fat, and use in stews and stir-fries or on skewers. Package them in 1lb/450g portions (or a size to suit your household) and freeze until needed.

Pork cut in cubes cooks much faster than chops or a roast, making this ideal for a quick family dinner. Add dried hot chilli peppers to taste and other vegetables, such as aubergine or courgette in season. Serve with boiled potatoes or over hot noodles.

1 lb	boneless pork (shoulder), cubed	450 g
1 tsp	vegetable oil	5 ml
1	large onion, coarsely chopped	1
1	garlic clove, chopped	1
1	can (14 oz/400 g) tomatoes	1
1	small sweet green pepper, coarsely chopped	1
2 tbsp	chopped fresh parsley	30 ml
½ tsp	crumbled dried cumin	2 ml
½ tsp	leaf oregano	2 ml
¼ tsp	thyme	1 ml
	Salt and freshly ground pepper	

Cut off any visible fat from pork. In heavy saucepan or frying pan, heat oil over medium-high heat; add pork a few pieces at a time and cook until lightly browned on all sides. (There should be enough fat in pork to prevent burning—a heavy or nonstick pan is important.) Add onion and garlic; cook, stirring, until onion is tender, about 2 minutes.

Stir in green pepper, tomatoes, parsley, cumin, oregano, thyme, and salt and pepper to taste. Bring to a boil; reduce heat and simmer, covered, for 15 minutes. Makes 4 servings.

Calories per serving: 252
Grams fat per serving: 13.6
Vitamins A and C, niacin and thiamin: Excellent
Iron and phosphorus: Good

Fresh Ginger

Whenever possible, use fresh, not ground, ginger in recipes—the flavour is far superior. Fresh ginger can elevate an ordinary dish into something really delicious. Use it in stir-fries, with vegetables, and in stuffings, stews and other savoury dishes. This brown, knobby root is available in the vegetable section of most supermarkets and fruit and vegetable stores.

To buy: Buy young ginger with pale brown skin. Shriveled skin is a sign of age. Avoid buying ginger with cracks, mould or a musty smell.

To store: Wrap ginger in a plastic bag to prevent drying out and store in a cool place or refrigerate for a few weeks. For longer storage, freeze ginger, or peel, place in a jar and cover with sherry or vodka; seal and refrigerate.

To use: With a vegetable peeler or knife, peel skin from portion of root you plan to use. Depending on the recipe, either grate or chop it before adding to the dish. Sometimes a slice of fresh ginger is added to a marinade or stew, then discarded before serving.

My children enjoy this dish because it isn't very spicy. You may want to add sherry, dried chilli peppers or perhaps more ginger to taste. Serve on a bed of hot fluffy rice.

1 tbsp	cooking oil	15 ml
1 lb	lean boneless pork, cut in thin strips	450 g
2	garlic cloves, chopped	2
1	onion, sliced	1
5	celery stalks, diagonally sliced	5
4	carrots, diagonally sliced	4
1 tbsp	peeled and grated fresh ginger root	15 ml
8 fl oz	hot chicken stock	250 ml
2 tbsp	low-sodium soy sauce	30 ml
¼ tsp	freshly ground pepper	1 ml
1	small head cabbage	1
1 tbsp	cornflour	15 ml
2 tbsp	cold water	30 ml
	Lemon juice	
	Salt and freshly ground pepper	

In wok or large heavy frying pan, heat oil over high heat. Add pork and stir-fry until pork is no longer pink. Add garlic, onion, celery, carrots and ginger; stir-fry until onion is tender. Add stock, soy sauce and pepper. Cover, and simmer for 5 minutes.

Shred cabbage. Stir into frying pan and cook for 3 to 4 minutes longer or until vegetables are tender-crisp. Blend cornflour with cold water; gradually add to frying pan stirring constantly, until sauce thickens. Add lemon juice, salt and pepper to taste. Makes 5 servings.

Calories per serving: 279
Grams fat per serving: 14
Fibre: Excellent
Thiamin, niacin and vitamins A and C: Excellent
Iron, riboflavin, and phosphorus: Good

PORK TENDERLOIN WITH ROSEMARY AND THYME

Pork tenderloin is the leanest cut of pork with little fat. This very quick and easy-to-prepare dish is ideal for a casual Friday night dinner party. In autumn, serve with pumpkin or sweet peppers, in summer with Tomatoes Provençal (page 153), in spring with Asparagus with Red Pepper Purée (pages 154–5) and in winter with Braised Red Cabbage (page 157).

2 tbsp	Dijon mustard	30 ml
1 tsp	rosemary	5 ml
½ tsp	thyme	2 ml
¼ tsp	whole black peppercorns, crushed	1 ml
1 lb	pork tenderloin	450 g

In small bowl, combine mustard, rosemary, thyme and peppercorns and mix. Spread over pork. Place in roasting pan. Roast in 350°F/180°C/Gas Mark 4 oven for 35 to 45 minutes or until no longer pink inside. Garnish with fresh rosemary. To serve, cut in thin slices. Makes 3 servings.

Calories per serving: 248
Grams fat per serving: 14
Iron, thiamin and niacin: Excellent
Phosphorus: Good

To reduce fat
- Buy lean cuts of pork.
- Trim visible fat before cooking.

Compare	4 oz/125 g serving Grams fat
Spareribs	44
Pork chop—lean and fat	37
Pork chop—lean only, fat removed	13
Pork tenderloin	9

SHERRY-BRAISED HAM WITH CURRIED FRUIT

Easter Dinner
Crudités with Creamy Fresh
Dill Dip (page 30)
Sherry-Braised Ham with
Curried Fruit (page 112)
Rice
Green beans
Lemon Charlotte with
Strawberries (page 202)

Warning: Because of the nitrites in most hams, ham should be eaten only occasionally and in moderation.

This is one of my best entertaining dishes for a large group. If you remove the fat before cooking, there will be less salt as well as less fat. Cooking ham in liquid makes it very juicy and tender.

1	cooked ham (9 lb/4 kg)	1
1	large onion, sliced	1
2	carrots, sliced	2
1 pt	beef stock	600 ml
8 tbsp	sherry	120 ml
1	bay leaf	1
$\frac{1}{2}$ tsp	thyme	2 ml
1	bunch watercress	1
	Curried Fruit with Rice (page 171)	

Remove skin and all but a very thin layer of fat covering ham. Place ham in roasting pan; arrange vegetables around it. Pour beef stock and sherry over ham; add bay leaf and thyme. Bring to a boil on top of stove. Cover and bake in 325°F/160°C/Gas Mark 3 oven for $2\frac{1}{2}$ hours, basting 3 or 4 times during roasting. Uncover and cook for 15 minutes longer. Remove from oven; transfer to platter and let stand for at least 15 minutes before carving (discard vegetables in pan).

Slice ham into thin slices. Garnish platter with watercress and be sure to include a sprig on each person's plate. Arrange hot curried fruit and rice on another plate. Makes about 18 servings.

Calories per serving 3½ oz/90 g: 186
Grams fat per serving: 8.1
Vitamin A, iron, niacin and thiamin: Excellent
Riboflavin: Good

GINGER AND APRICOT STUFFED LAMB WITH KUMQUATS

Bright orange, grape-sized kumquats are a most attractive edible garnish for this dish. Make it in the spring when kumquats are readily available.

1	boneless leg of shoulder of lamb (3 lb/1.4 kg), ready for stuffing (about 5 lb/2.2 kg, bone-in)	1

Stuffing

½ oz	butter	12 g
1	small onion, chopped	1
4 oz	coarsely chopped dried apricots	125 g
1 tbsp	peeled and grated fresh ginger root	15 ml
1 tsp	grated lemon rind	5 ml
	Salt and freshly ground pepper	

Glaze

2 tbsp	apricot jam	30 ml
½ tsp	Dijon mustard	2 ml
¼ tsp	ground ginger	1 ml

Garnish

8	apricots (fresh or canned), halved and pitted	8
8	sprigs fresh rosemary or watercress	8
8	small ripe kumquats (optional)	8

Stuffing: In small frying pan, melt butter over medium heat; add onion and cook until soft. Stir in apricots, ginger, lemon rind, and salt and pepper to taste. Place stuffing in lamb cavity and sew or tie together. Place on rack in baking pan. Roast in 325°F/160°C/Gas Mark 3 oven for 1½ hours.

Glaze: Combine jam, mustard and ginger; mix well. Brush over outside of lamb and continue roasting for 15 minutes longer or until lamb is brown outside and pink inside. Transfer to serving platter and let stand for 15 minutes before carving. Arrange halved apricots, rosemary sprigs and whole unpeeled kumquats around lamb. Makes 8 servings.

Calories per serving: 326
Grams fat per serving: 10
Fibre: Good
Vitamin A and niacin: Excellent
Iron, thiamin, phosphorus and riboflavin: Good

MARINATED LEG OF LAMB WITH CORIANDER

Should lamb be rare or well-done?
As with beef, this is a matter of personal taste. However, if it is too rare, it can be tough. If overcooked, it will be dry. The safest is medium-rare—it will be tender, juicy and pink on the inside.

Boneless butterflied legs of lamb are available in the chilled food sections of many supermarkets or fresh at your local butcher. This marinade is also delicious with lamb chops and rack of lamb. An easy dish to prepare in advance, marinated leg of lamb is also easy to transport (in a plastic bag) to the holiday home or barbecue.

1	boneless butterflied leg of lamb (about $3\frac{1}{2}$ lb/1.6 kg)	1
	Salt and freshly ground pepper	
	Dijon mustard or Bramble Sauce (page 147)	
Marinade		
1 tbsp	coriander seeds	15 ml
8 tbsp	lemon juice	120 ml
2 tbsp	vegetable oil	30 ml
1	small onion, chopped	1
1 tbsp	grated fresh ginger root	15 ml
2	garlic cloves, chopped	2
1 tsp	black peppercorns, crushed	5 ml

Marinade: In frying pan, toast coriander seeds over medium heat for 5 minutes, shaking pan occasionally. Remove from heat; let cool, then crush seeds. Combine crushed seeds, lemon juice, oil, onion, ginger, garlic and peppercorns.

Cut off any fat from lamb and discard. If meat is not of even thickness, slash thickest section and open up. Place lamb in glass or ceramic dish or plastic bag and coat both sides of meat with marinade. Cover and refrigerate for 48 hours, turning once. Remove lamb from refrigerator about 1 hour before cooking.

Drain lamb and wipe dry. Place on grilling rack or barbecue grill about 6 inches/15 cm from heat for about 12 minutes on each side for medium-rare, 15 to 20 minutes on each side for well-done. Meat thermometer should register 140°F/60°C for rare, 160°F/70°C for medium and 180°F/80°C for well-done. Remove from heat; let stand for 5 minutes, season with salt and pepper to taste, then slice thinly across the grain. Serve with Dijon mustard or Bramble Sauce (page 147). Makes 8 servings.

Calories per (5 oz/140 g) serving: 393
Grams fat per serving: 11
Iron, riboflavin, phosphorus, niacin and thiamin: Excellent
Vitamin C: Good

SOUVLAKIA OF LAMB

Greece is famous for its souvlakia or skewered lamb, which the Greeks season with lemon juice and oregano. They don't usually have vegetables on the skewers, but it's more colourful when you include them and they add extra bite. Serve the skewers on hot rice.

1 lb	boneless lamb loin	450 g
2 tbsp	lemon juice	30 ml
1 tsp	oregano	5 ml
	Salt and freshly ground pepper	
8	small onions	8
1	small red pepper	1
1	small yellow or green pepper	1

Cut lamb into 1 inch/2.5 cm cubes. Place in glass dish or plate and sprinkle with lemon juice, oregano, and salt and pepper to taste. Blanch onions in boiling water for 10 to 15 minutes or until almost tender; drain. When cool enough to handle, cut off root ends of onions and squeeze off skins. Seed peppers and cut into $1\frac{1}{2}$ inch/4 cm pieces.

Thread lamb alternating with vegetables onto flat-bladed metal skewers or wooden skewers that have been soaked in water.

Preheat grill. Place skewers on grilling rack and cook about 5 inches/13 cm from heat, turning every 3 to 4 minutes, for 12 minutes or until meat is brown outside but still pink inside. Makes 4 servings.

Calories per serving: 224
Grams fat per serving: 7
Fibre: Good
Niacin and vitamins A and C: Excellent
Iron and phosphorus: Good

NAVARIN OF LAMB

When the International Association of Cooking Professionals held their annual conference in 1984, sixteen food writers and teachers entertained delegates in their homes for dinner. We all served the same menu and the main course was Lucy Waverman's delicious Navarin of Lamb and wild rice. This version is adapted from her recipe. The garlic is sweet and mild, and fresh rosemary adds a very special flavour. Serve with rice noodles or potatoes.

2 lb	lean boneless lamb (e.g. leg) cubed	1 kg
1 tsp	granulated sugar	5 ml
	Salt and freshly ground pepper	
1 tbsp	vegetable oil	15 ml
2 tbsp	plain flour	30 ml
16 fl oz	beef or lamb stock	500 ml
1	garlic clove, chopped	1
1 tbsp	tomato purée	15 ml
	Bouquet garni*	
1	long strip orange rind (orange part only)	1
1 tbsp	fresh rosemary leaves or 1 tsp/5ml dried	15 ml
Vegetables		
5	carrots	5
3	small white turnips or 1 swede (about 1 lb/450 g)	3
10	small onions	10
Garlic Garnish		
4	heads garlic	4
4 fl oz	milk	125 ml

Trim any fat from lamb; sprinkle with sugar, and salt and pepper. In large heavy nonstick pan, heat oil over medium heat until hot. Add meat a few pieces at a time and brown well.

Remove meat from pan and pour off all fat. Return meat to pan; add flour and cook over medium heat, stirring constantly, for 1 minute or until flour has browned. Add stock, garlic, tomato purée, bouquet garni and orange rind.

Bring to a boil, stirring to scrape up all the tasty brown bits from bottom of pan. Cover and bake in 325°F/160°C/Gas Mark 3 oven for 1 hour. Let cool, then refrigerate overnight or until cold.

Remove fat from surface of stew; discard orange rind and bouquet garni.

Vegetables: Scrape carrots; peel turnips and onions. Cut carrots and turnips into ¾ inch/2 cm pieces.

Garlic Garnish: Separate garlic heads into cloves. Combine garlic with milk in small saucepan. Bring to a boil and boil for 2 minutes. Reduce heat to low; cover and simmer until garlic cloves are soft. Drain. When cool, gently squeeze cloves to remove skins. Set aside.

About 45 minutes before serving, gently reheat lamb mixture, stirring to prevent burning. Add vegetables and simmer, covered, for 30 minutes or until vegetables are tender; add water if necessary. (For a thicker gravy, add 2 tbsp/30 ml flour mixed with 4 fl oz/125 ml water or stock; bring to a boil and cook, stirring, until thickened slightly.) Add rosemary and garnish with garlic cloves. Makes 8 servings.

Calories per serving: 261
Grams fat per serving: 11
Fibre: Good
Vitamins A and C and niacin: Excellent
Iron and phosphorus: Good

FISH

When it comes to fish, we don't know how lucky we are. Supplies are plentiful and the variety is enormous, and being an island, means fresh fish straight from the sea doesn't have far to travel inland. And when I say fresh, I mean no more than a day or two out of the water. Be careful with the meaning of the word fresh. Sometimes we say fresh to mean not frozen, but just because a fish has not yet been frozen it's not necessarily fresh—it may have been out of the water for days.

The best test of a fresh fish is its smell. It should be very mildly fishy, nothing stronger. Don't hesitate to ask to smell the fish; a reputable fishmonger will encourage your scrutiny, and you'll discover it pays to find a fishmonger you can rely on.

If you can't get good fresh fish, don't let that prevent you from enjoying fish. Frozen fish is available right across the country. Part of the trick of cooking frozen fish is defrosting it properly. Don't put it out on the work surface hours before you plan to cook it. It's important to keep fish cold so the outside portions don't deteriorate while the inside is still frozen. The best method of defrosting it is to place fish in the refrigerator. Often we don't have the time, so the next best way is to immerse the package in cold water for about 1½ hours. That way the outside thawed portion stays cold while the centre is still defrosting. Before cooking, separate the fish into fillets if it has been frozen in a block; it looks more appealing that way.

There is an unnecessary mystique about cooking fish—too many people are afraid to take the plunge when in fact fish is one of the easiest foods to cook. With fish, the simpler the better. Most fish has a delicate flavour that you don't want to mask with strong seasonings or heavy sauces. A sprinkling of lemon juice and chopped fresh parsley is a classic, delicious preparation. Just try Sole Fillets with Lemon and Parsley (page 119).

There is one very simple tip for cooking perfect fish every time, which means you no longer have to guess how long to cook it. Measure the thickness of the fish at the thickest part; for each inch/2.5 cm of thickness, allow 10 minutes of cooking time at 400°F/200°C/Gas Mark 6; add 5 minutes if the fish is wrapped in foil. Perfectly cooked fish is opaque and flakes slightly. Avoid overcooking; it dries the fish out.

Best of all, fish is healthy—it's low in fat and calories and high in protein, and for cooks on the move it's one of the fastest foods around.

SOLE FILLETS WITH LEMON AND PARSLEY

*Haddock, plaice or cod may be substituted for the sole.

Fish is an excellent source of protein and is low in fat and calories.

This is such a simple recipe, yet it's one of the very best ways to make tender, moist fish fillets. If using frozen fillets, try to thaw and separate them before cooking for best results.

1 lb	sole fillets*	450 g
	Salt and freshly ground pepper	
1 oz	butter, melted	25 g
2 tbsp	chopped fresh parsley	30 ml
1 tbsp	lemon juice	15 ml

Place fillets in lightly oiled baking dish just large enough to hold them in a single layer. Sprinkle with salt and pepper to taste. Combine butter, parsley and lemon juice. Drizzle over fish. Bake, uncovered, in 450°F/230°C/Gas Mark 8 oven for 8 to 10 minutes (10 minutes per inch thickness for fresh fish) or until fish is opaque and flakes easily. To microwave: Cover with greaseproof paper wrap and turn back corner to vent for steam; microwave on High for 3½ to 4½ minutes (the times vary with the model you own). Makes 4 servings.

Calories per serving: 117
Grams fat per serving: 7

SOLE FLORENTINE

This colourful dish is a little fancier than Sole Fillets with Lemon and Parsley. You can prepare it in advance, then bake it just before serving.

1¼ lb	sole fillets	575 g
1	onion, chopped	1
½	bay leaf	½
2 tbsp	lemon juice	30 ml
3	peppercorns	3
½ tsp	salt	2 ml
6 fl oz	dry white wine	175 ml
1 lb	fresh spinach	450 g
½ oz	butter	15 g
2 tbsp	plain flour	30 ml
4 fl oz	milk	125 ml
	Salt and freshly ground pepper	
1 tbsp	grated Parmesan cheese	15 ml

Roll up fillets and secure with cocktail sticks. Arrange rolls in pan just large enough to hold them in single layers; add onion, bay leaf, lemon juice, peppercorns and salt. Pour in wine; bring to a boil. Cover, reduce heat and simmer for 5 minutes. Remove fillets from liquid, reserving liquid.

Wash spinach; cook, covered, in saucepan in just the water clinging to leaves. Drain, and squeeze out excess water; chop finely.

Place spinach in shallow greased dish just large enough to hold the fish rolls. Place fish on top of spinach.

Strain reserved poaching liquid; measure 8 fl oz/250 ml (add water if necessary). In small saucepan, melt butter; add flour and stir over low heat for 1 minute. Whisk in poaching liquid, milk, and salt and pepper to taste. Bring to a boil, stirring constantly. Remove from heat. (It may be prepared ahead to this point and reheated.)

Pour sauce over fish and sprinkle with Parmesan cheese. Bake in 375°F/190°C/Gas Mark 5 oven for 10 to 20 minutes or until bubbly. Makes 4 servings.

Calories per serving: 226
Grams fat per serving: 7
Fibre: Excellent
Vitamins A and C: Excellent
Iron and riboflavin: Good

Opposite:
Pork Tenderloin with Rosemary and Thyme (page 111), Asparagus with Red Pepper Purée (pages 154–155)

CAPELLINI WITH CLAM SAUCE AND SWEET RED PEPPERS

Capellini are the thinnest of noodles, but this recipe works well with any kind of noodle. Wholewheat noodles are good because of their higher fibre content. Serve this extremely easy-to-make dish with steamed mangetout or tossed spinach salad. This is perfect for unexpected guests—the ingredients keep well, and it's so fast to prepare.

2	sweet red peppers	2
½ oz	butter	15 g
3	garlic cloves, chopped	3
	Salt and freshly ground pepper	
8 fl oz	dry white wine	250 ml
1	can (5 oz/142 g) clams, drained	1
1 tsp	fresh thyme leaves or ¼ tsp/1 ml dried	5 ml
1 oz	fresh parsley, chopped	25 g
8 oz	capellini (fresh or dried)	225 g
3 tbsp	grated Parmesan cheese	45 ml

Core and seed red peppers; cut into thin strips.

In heavy frying pan, melt half the butter; add red peppers and 1 clove of garlic. Cook over medium heat, stirring often, until peppers are tender, about 10 minutes. Season with salt and pepper to taste.

In saucepan, melt remaining butter over medium heat; add remaining garlic and cook, stirring, for 1 minute. Add wine, clams and thyme; simmer for 5 minutes. Add parsley, and salt and pepper to taste.

Meanwhile, in large pot of boiling water, cook capellini until al dente (tender but firm); drain. Spoon capellini onto warmed dinner plates. Pour sauce over it. Arrange sautéed red peppers around pasta. Sprinkle pasta with Parmesan. Serve immediately. Makes 3 main-course or 6 appetizer servings.

	Main Course	Appetizer
Calories per serving:	275	138
Grams fat per serving:	9	4.5
Iron: Excellent		
Vitamins A and C and phosphorus: Good		

Opposite:
Sole Fillets with Lemon and Parsley (page 119), Herbed Green Beans with Garlic (page 160), Cracked Wheat and Basil Pilaf (page 173)

MUSSELS SICILIAN STYLE

How to Buy and Store Mussels
It's unbelievable that shellfish as tender and delicious as mussels are relatively inexpensive. Buy medium-sized (about 18 to the pound/450 g) cultured mussels—they're much easier to clean and have more meat than the wild ones. Only buy mussels that have closed shells. The fresher the mussels, the better they taste. However, they can be kept in a bowl or paper (not plastic) bag in the refrigerator for two or three days. Serve as a first course or a main course.

For a delightfully easy supper, buy fresh mussels on your way home from work and serve this dish with fresh bread and salad. If you buy cultured mussels, they take only minutes to clean and supper can be ready in 15 minutes.

2 lb	fresh mussels (about 36)	1 kg
1 tsp	olive oil	5 ml
1	small onion, finely chopped	1
1	large garlic clove, chopped	1
Pinch	each dried thyme and oregano	Pinch
1	can (14 oz/400 g) or 4 fresh tomatoes, coarsely chopped	1
4 tbsp	dry white wine	60 ml
½ oz	chopped fresh parsley	15 g

Scrub mussels under cold water and pull off hairy beards. In large heavy saucepan, heat oil over medium heat; add onion and garlic and cook for 2 to 3 minutes or until tender. Stir in thyme and oregano; add tomatoes, breaking up tomatoes with back of spoon. Bring to a boil and boil for about 2 minutes to reduce liquid. Add wine and return to a boil. Add mussels; cover and cook for 5 minutes or until shells open and mussels are cooked. Discard any shells that don't open. Sprinkle with parsley.

Ladle mussels into large soup bowls, spooning tomato mixture over them. Eat with a fork and a spoon—the fork to pull the mussels out of their shells, the spoon to consume the heavenly broth. Or, sop up remaining broth with bread. Makes 2 servings.

Calories per serving: 223
Grams fat per serving: 6
Fibre: Good
Vitamins A and C, iron, niacin and phosphorus: Excellent
Calcium and thiamin: Good

LINGUINE WITH PRAWNS AND TOMATO

Cooking Pasta

Cook pasta in a large pot of boiling salted water, using about 6–6½ pts/4 L of water for every pound/450 g of pasta. Add pasta a little at a time so the water doesn't stop boiling, and stir with a fork to make sure noodles don't stick together.

Fresh pasta cooks quickly sometimes in as little time as 2 minutes. Dried pasta takes longer, usually at least 7 minutes, sometimes 10 to 12 minutes. Begin tasting to see whether pasta is done before the suggested cooking time; pasta is cooked when it's al dente (tender but firm—not mushy) and has lost its raw starch taste. Drain in a colander, then toss immediately with sauce, butter or oil as specified in recipe to prèvent pasta from sticking together. Because pasta cools quickly, it's important to warm the platter or individual plates it's to be served on. For cold pasta salad, rinse pasta under cold running water to prevent sticking.

Be sure to have the sauce ready before the pasta is finished cooking (overcooked, soft, gluey pasta isn't appealing); then toss pasta with sauce and serve immediately.

The idea for this recipe came from caterer Dinah Koo. The prawns and tomato should be quickly cooked over high heat to preserve flavour and texture. If using fresh pasta, make sauce first, because the pasta cooks so quickly.

4 oz	linguine or wholewheat noodles	125 g
1 tbsp	vegetable oil	15 ml
1	large garlic clove, chopped	1
2 tbsp	finely chopped shallots	30 ml
2	large tomatoes, coarsely chopped	2
¼ tsp	dried basil, or fresh, chopped, to taste	1 ml
4 oz	small or medium prawns, peeled (raw or cooked)	125 g
1 or 2	spring onions, chopped	1 or 2
	Salt and freshly ground pepper	

In a large pot of boiling water, cook linguine until al dente (tender but firm) or according to package directions; drain.

Meanwhile, in heavy frying pan, heat oil over high heat. Add garlic and shallots; cook, stirring, for about 30 seconds. Add tomatoes and basil; cook, stirring, for about 1 minute. Add prawns and cook, stirring, until prawns are hot and, if using raw, they turn pink. Sprinkle with spring onions and season with salt and pepper to taste. Spoon over hot linguine. Makes 2 servings.

Calories per serving: 395
Grams fat per serving: 8
Fibre: Good
Iron, thiamin, niacin and vitamin C: Excellent
Vitamin A and phosphorus: Good

SCALLOPS AND PRAWNS IN WINE BOUILLON WITH JULIENNE VEGETABLES

Special Spring Dinner
Asparagus with Red Pepper Purée (pages 154–5)
Scallops and Prawns in Wine Bouillon with Julienne Vegetables (pages 124–5) or Sole Florentine (page 120)
Strawberries with Raspberry and Rhubarb Sauce (page 220)

Serve this elegant nouvelle cuisine dish for a special dinner. It's the only recipe in the book with double cream; the cream is optional, but it does add a delicious smoothness and rich flavour. Luckily, the rest of the ingredients are low in fat.

12 oz	large raw prawns	350 g
16	mussels (optional)	16
2	medium carrots	2
1	sweet red pepper	1
2	leeks (white part only)	2
1	small courgette	1
$\frac{1}{2}$ oz	butter	15 g
3	shallots, finely chopped	3
2	large garlic cloves, chopped	2
4 fl oz	white wine	125 ml
8 oz	scallops	225 g
2 oz	finely chopped fresh parsley	50 g
4 fl oz	double cream (optional)	125 ml
	Salt and freshly ground pepper	
10 oz	hot cooked rice	300 g

Shell prawns and remove intestinal tract running down back. Scrub mussels and pull off hairy beards. Peel carrots. Seed pepper. Cut leek lengthwise halfway, then wash under cold running water. Cut ends from courgette. Cut all vegetables into julienne strips (like matchsticks). Blanch vegetables in boiling water for 2 minutes; drain. Plunge into a bowl of ice water to cool; drain.

In large heavy saucepan or flameproof casserole, melt the butter; stir in shallots and garlic and cook over medium-low heat, stirring, for 3 to 5 minutes or until tender. Add wine; bring to a boil. Add prawns, mussels, scallops and parsley; cover, and simmer for about 3 minutes or until prawns turn pink and scallops are opaque. Discard any mussels that do not open. Be careful not to overcook or seafood will be tough. Pour in cream (if using) and vegetables and cook until hot.

Be very careful not to overcook scallops. They cook very fast and in just a minute can change from tender to tough and rubbery. They're cooked when they become opaque.

Although scallops are low in fat, they are high in cholesterol. Therefore, they shouldn't be eaten too often.

4 fl oz/125 ml whipping cream added to the sauce is scrumptious but adds 8 grams fat per serving.

Taste liquid in pan and add salt and pepper. If liquid is too thin, thicken it by adding 2 tsp/10 ml cornflour mixed with 2 tbsp/30 ml water; stir and bring to a boil.

Serve in shallow bowls or with rice or noodles. Makes 4 servings.

	Without cream	With cream
Calories per serving:	415	515
Grams fat per serving:	6.5	14.5

Fibre: Good
Vitamin A, niacin and iron: Excellent
Thiamin and calcium: Good

BAKED SALMON WITH HERBS

*Plan on about $\frac{1}{2}$ lb/225 g per person for a salmon under 4 lb/2 kg; or about 6 oz//175 g per person for a salmon over 4 lb/2 kg or a chunk piece.

When buying a whole fish, ask the fishmonger to clean and scale it. If you don't want the head left on, ask him to cut it off. If you want fillets, the fishmonger will usually fillet the fish for you, and sometimes will even remove the backbone and yet leave the fish whole. (Fillets are boneless pieces of fish cut from either side of the backbone; steaks are cut crosswise and include some bone.)

One of my favourite dinner party menus is a baked whole salmon. It's about the easiest main course dish to prepare, and it is elegant and delicious. When serving four to six people, arrange hot cooked vegetables such as green beans or mangetout on a platter alongside the salmon. It will look like a sumptuous feast.

1	whole salmon or piece about $2\frac{1}{2}$ lb/1.2 kg*	1
1 oz	chopped fresh parsley	25 g
2 tbsp	combination of chopped fresh herbs—dill, chives, chervil, basil, sage (optional)	30 ml
	Salt and freshly ground pepper	
1 tbsp	water	15 ml
1 tbsp	lemon juice	15 ml
Garnish (optional)		
	Cucumber slices, parsley, dill or watercress	

Place salmon on foil; measure thickness at thickest part. Sprinkle parsley and herbs, and salt and pepper to taste inside cavity. Mix water with lemon juice and sprinkle over outside of salmon. Fold foil over and seal.

Place wrapped salmon on baking sheet and bake in 450°F/230°C/Gas Mark 8 oven for 10 minutes for every 1 inch/2.5 cm thickness of fish, plus an additional 10 minutes' cooking time because it's wrapped in foil (35 to 40 minutes' total cooking time), or until salmon is opaque. Unwrap salmon and discard skin; most of it should stick to foil. Place salmon on warmed platter. Garnish with cucumber, parsley, dill or watercress (if using). Alternatively, arrange cooked vegetables on platter with salmon.

Serve warm with Yogurt Hollandaise (page 150), Creamy Fresh Dill Dip (page 30) or lemon wedges.

To serve cold: While salmon is still warm, discard skin and scrape off any dark fat. Brush salmon lightly with oil and cover with foil. Refrigerate until serving time. Makes about 4 servings.

Dinner Party for Six
Fresh Tomato and Dill Bisque
(page 38)
Baked Salmon with Herbs
(pages 126–7)
Rice or tiny potatoes in skins
Herbed Green Beans with
Garlic (page 160)
Frozen Lemon Cream
(page 195) with Raspberry
Coulis (page 193)

Calories per serving: 391
Grams fat per serving: 16
Vitamin C, niacin and phosphorus: Excellent
Thiamin, calcium, iron and vitamin A: Good
These are large-size servings: 3 oz/90 g of cooked (steamed or baked) salmon has 7 grams fat.

SOLE POACHED WITH TOMATOES, ARTICHOKES AND MUSHROOMS

You can use any type of white fish fillets or steaks, such as cod, halibut or haddock, in this moist and savoury fish dish. Serve over pasta or rice.

½ oz	butter	15 g
4 oz	thickly sliced mushrooms	125 g
1	garlic clove, chopped	1
3	tomatoes, seeded and cut in chunks	3
½ tsp	basil	2 ml
Pinch	thyme	Pinch
1 lb	sole fillets	450 g
1	can (14 oz/400 g) artichoke hearts, drained and halved	1
	Salt and freshly ground pepper	
	Granulated sugar (optional)	

In heavy saucepan or frying pan, melt butter; cook mushrooms and garlic over medium-high heat, shaking pan or stirring, until mushrooms are tender.

Add tomatoes, basil and thyme; bring to a simmer. Add sole and artichokes; cover and simmer for 3 minutes. Uncover and cook for 5 minutes longer or until fish is opaque. Season with salt and pepper to taste (add pinch of sugar if tomatoes are too acidic). Makes 4 servings.

Calories per serving: 141
Grams fat per serving: 5
Vitamin C: Excellent
Vitamin A: Good

MICROWAVE FILLETS PROVENÇAL

Use any lean fish fillets—plaice, whiting, sole, cod, haddock or monkfish. It's best to use fresh fillets if available, but you can use frozen.

1	can (14 oz/400 g) tomatoes	1
1 lb	fish fillets	450 g
	Salt and freshly ground pepper	
½ oz	chopped fresh parsley	15 g
4 tbsp	fine fresh bread crumbs	60 ml
2	spring onions (including tops), chopped	2
½ oz	butter, melted	15 g
2	garlic cloves, chopped	2

Drain and coarsely chop tomatoes. In microwave dish just large enough to hold fillets in single layer, spoon half the tomatoes. Arrange fillets on top and sprinkle with salt and pepper to taste. Top with remaining tomatoes.

In small bowl, combine parsley, bread crumbs, onions, butter and garlic; sprinkle over tomatoes. Partially cover and microwave on High for 9 to 12 minutes or until fish is opaque. Let stand for 3 minutes before serving. Makes 4 servings.

Note: To cook in conventional oven, bake in 450°F/230°C/Gas Mark 8 oven for 20 minutes for fresh fillets, 40 minutes for frozen, or until fish is opaque.

Calories per serving: 244
Grams fat per serving: 9
Vitamins A and C, niacin and phosphorus: Excellent

BROCHETTES OF SALMON AND PRAWNS

For other fish dishes, see:
Fish Chowder, Family Style
(page 54)
Seafood Chowder (page 48)
Fettuccine with Clam Sauce
(page 108)

Serve these skewers of salmon and prawns over a bed of rice. Either add the vegetables to the skewers or arrange them artistically around the plate. Creamy Fresh Dill Dip (page 30) goes well with this.

1½ lb	salmon, skin removed, cut in ¾ inch/2 cm cubes	675 g
16	raw prawns (about 1 lb/450 g)	16
8	stalks asparagus or 16 cherry tomatoes	8
16	large mushrooms	16
16	large seedless green grapes	16
3 tbsp	vegetable oil	45 ml
1 tbsp	lime juice	15 ml
1	garlic clove, chopped	1
	Salt and freshly ground pepper	

Snap off tough ends of asparagus. Peel stalks if desired. Blanch in boiling water for 3 minutes; drain. Cut into 1½ inch/4 cm lengths. On thin (preferably wooden) skewers, thread pieces of salmon and prawns, alternating with asparagus, mushrooms and grapes.

Combine oil, lime juice, garlic, and salt and pepper to taste; brush over skewers. Grill for about 10 to 15 minutes or until fish is opaque. Alternatively, place skewers on wire rack set over boiling water in grill pan; cover with foil and steam for 10 to 15 minutes or until fish is opaque. Sprinkle with salt and pepper. Makes 6 main course or 8 appetizer servings.

Calories per main course serving: 233
Grams fat per main course serving: 9.3
Niacin: Excellent
Iron, phosphorus and calcium: Good

Types of Fish

Low-fat fish
— red snapper
— scallops
— plaice
— cod
— sole
— monkfish
— whiting
— haddock

Medium-fat fish
— halibut
— pilchards
— trout
— lobster
— tuna
— skate

Fat fish
— herring
— turbot
— kipper
— salmon
— mackerel
— sardines

Buying Fresh Fish
When possible buy fish the day you want to cook it. The best test for freshness is to use your nose—the fish should have a mild fishy or seawater odour. Anything stronger means the fish has been out of the water for too long.

Look for
• mild smell
• glistening, firm flesh that springs back when touched
• very firmly attached scales
• clear, bright convex eyes (not sunken)

Buying Frozen Fish
Look for
• glazed fish coated with ice
• shiny, solidly frozen flesh with no signs of drying or freezer burn (white spots)
• tightly wrapped package with no sign of frost or ice crystals inside.

Storing Fresh Fish
• If not cleaned, clean as soon as possible.
• Wipe with a damp cloth, wrap in greaseproof paper or cling film and place in covered container.
• Store in coldest part of the refrigerator.
• Cook as soon as possible (same day for shop bought, within 4 days if freshly caught).

Storing Frozen Fish
• Keep fish at 0°F/−18°C or lower for ideal storage.
• Store fat fish (salmon, mackerel, trout) for a maximum of 2 months.
• Store lean fish (cod, haddock, sole, plaice) for a maximum of 6 months.

How to Cook Fish
• Measure fish at the thickest part (stuffed or not).
• Allow for 10 minutes' cooking time per inch/2.5 cm thickness for fresh fish; double the time if fish is frozen. If wrapped in foil, add 5 minutes for fresh, 10 minutes for frozen. This applies to all fish and cooking methods (if in oven, cook at 450°F/230°C/Gas Mark 8).

Methods of Cooking Fish
Steaming (top of stove)
Pour 2 inches/5 cm of water in a steamer and bring to a boil. Season and wrap fish securely in cheesecloth. Place on a rack over boiling water. Cover and begin timing (see above).

Oven steaming
Preheat oven to 450°F/230°C/Gas Mark 8. Place fresh or frozen fish on lightly greased foil. Season to taste with salt, pepper and herbs (parsley, dill, chives or basil). Sprinkle with lemon juice or white wine. Wrap securely. Place on a baking sheet and bake for required cooking time (see above), adding 5 minutes for fresh and 10 minutes for frozen fish because of being wrapped in foil.

Poaching
Place fish on greased foil. Season with salt and pepper and add chopped onion and celery. Wrap, using double folds to make package watertight. Place in rapidly boiling water. Cover pan and return to boil; reduce heat and simmer for required cooking time (see above). Fish may also be wrapped in cheesecloth and poached in court bouillon or fish stock.)

To microwave fish
Place fish in glass dish. Season with salt and pepper to taste. Cover with greaseproof paper and turn back corners to allow steam to escape. Estimate cooking time at 3 to 4 minutes per pound/450 g, plus 2 to 3 minutes' standing time. Microwave on High or according to appliance manual.

Fish is cooked when it flakes and separates into solid moist sections when firmly prodded with a fork, and flesh is opaque.

MEATLESS ENTRÉES

Meatless entrées are nothing new. Macaroni and cheese and scrambled eggs have been family favourites for generations, and people who would never call themselves vegetarians often enjoy pizza without pepperoni.

It's becoming increasingly apparent that from both a health and a cost point of view one or more meatless dinners a week can be very beneficial. Also, meatless meals include a surprising variety of foods—everything from vegetables and pasta to eggs and cheese. For the inventive cook, the tasty combinations are endless. For the health conscious, meatless meals often offer lower fat and higher fibre and vitamin content than meat dishes, and, after all, that kind of eating is what this book is about. For other meatless main course recipes, be sure to check our soup, salad and vegetable suggestions.

Light Supper for a Winter's Day
Broccoli Frittata (pages 132–3)
Danish Cucumber Salad (page 65)
Wholewheat Irish Soda Bread (page 181)
Baked apples

BROCCOLI FRITTATA

This Italian open omelette is delicious for supper or lunch. Unlike a French omelette, which is cooked quickly over high heat and is creamy in the centre, a frittata is cooked slowly and is set or firm in the centre.

1 lb	broccoli	450 g
1 tbsp	vegetable oil	15 ml
1	large onion, sliced	1
2	garlic cloves, chopped	2
6	eggs, lightly beaten	6
1 tsp	salt	5 ml
Pinch	each nutmeg and freshly ground pepper	Pinch
3 oz	grated mozzarella cheese	75 g

Trim tough ends from broccoli and peel stems. Cut stems and florets into ¾ inch/2 cm pieces. Steam or cook broccoli in boiling water for 3 to 5 minutes or until crisp-tender; drain thoroughly.

In 10 inch/25 cm frying pan, preferably nonstick, heat oil; add onion and garlic and cook over medium heat until onion is tender. Stir in broccoli.

Broccoli is an excellent source of vitamins A and C and is associated with reduced risk of cancer of the colon.

Beat together eggs, salt, nutmeg and pepper; pour over broccoli mixture and sprinkle with cheese. Cover, and cook over medium-low heat for 5 to 10 minutes or until set but still slightly moist on top. Place under grill for 2 to 3 minutes to lightly brown top. (If the frying pan handle isn't ovenproof, wrap it in foil.) Loosen edges of frittata and cut into pie-shaped wedges. Makes 4 servings.

Calories per serving: 199
Grams fat per serving: 16
Fibre: Excellent
Vitamins A and C: Excellent
Riboflavin and niacin: Good

EGGS FLORENTINE

This delicious dish is perfect for brunch, lunch or a light supper. The eggs can be poached in advance, cooled in ice water to prevent further cooking and refrigerated in a bowl of water. Reheat them by placing in a pan of simmering water for about 30 seconds. The spinach and sauce can also be prepared in advance and gently reheated.

6 fl oz	Yogurt Hollandaise (pages 150–1)	175 ml
1¼ lb	spinach	575 g
½ oz	butter	15 g
	Salt and freshly ground pepper and freshly grated nutmeg	
2 tbsp	white wine vinegar	30 ml
6	eggs	6

Prepare Yogurt Hollandaise as directed and keep warm.

Wash spinach and discard stems; place leaves in saucepan. Cover and cook just in the water clinging to leaves, over medium-high heat until spinach is wilted. Drain thoroughly and chop spinach coarsely; toss with butter, and salt, pepper and nutmeg to taste. Return to saucepan, cover and keep warm. (If preparing in advance, drain, then cool under cold running water and drain again; reheat over low heat.)

Nearly fill a large shallow pan or frying pan with water and bring to a boil; add vinegar. Break eggs over pan and gently drop into water; reduce heat until water is barely simmering and cook eggs for 3 to 5 minutes or until whites are firm and yellows are still soft; spoon water over top of yolk occasionally to cook it slightly.

Spoon spinach onto warmed plates or serving dish. Remove eggs from water with slotted spoon. Place 1 egg over each portion of spinach. Spoon about 2 tbsp/30 ml of sauce over each egg and serve immediately. Makes 6 servings.

Calories per serving: 130
Grams fat per serving: 9
Fibre: Excellent
Vitamins A and C: Excellent
Iron and niacin: Good

Brunch or Lunch Menu
Grapefruit Juice Spritzer
(page 134)
Eggs Florentine (page 134)
Tomatoes Provençal (page 153)
Tossed green salad
Toasted Teacakes
Raspberry Meringue Torte
(page 206) or Pear Crisp with
Rolled Oats Topping (page 209)

Grapefruit Juice Spritzer
For a refreshing non-alcoholic drink that's perfect before lunch or brunch, combine equal parts of grapefruit juice and soda water. Serve over ice cubes and garnish with thin slices of lime.

Asparagus with Poached Eggs
In spring, substitute cooked drained asparagus for the spinach in Eggs Florentine. Arrange hot asparagus spears on warmed individual plates or serving dish; sprinkle with lemon juice, salt and pepper. Top with a poached egg and grated Parmesan cheese or Yogurt Hollandaise. If desired, place under grill for a minute to brown.

OMELETTE À LA JARDINIÈRE

This is delicious for a quick dinner or lunch. Serve with toasted wholewheat bread and a spinach salad.

1 tsp	vegetable oil	5 ml
1	small onion, finely chopped	1
1	garlic clove, chopped	1
1	carrot, grated	1
$\frac{1}{4}$	green pepper, chopped	$\frac{1}{4}$
	Salt and freshly ground pepper	
4	eggs	4
1 tbsp	water	15 ml
$\frac{1}{2}$ oz	butter	15 g
2 oz	alfalfa sprouts (or bean sprouts)	50 g

In frying pan, heat oil; sauté onion and garlic over medium heat, stirring, until tender. Stir in carrot and green pepper and stir-fry for about 3 minutes or until carrot has wilted. Season with salt and pepper to taste.

Beat eggs with water and a large pinch of salt and pepper until whites and yolks are thoroughly blended. Heat an 8 to 9 inch/20 to 23 cm nonstick omelette pan or frying pan over very high heat until pan is hot. Add butter to pan. When it sizzles but just before it starts to brown, pour in beaten eggs. Continuously shake the pan back and forth and at the same time stir eggs quickly with a fork to spread them evenly over bottom of pan as they thicken. When eggs have thickened and are almost set, spoon carrot mixture and alfalfa spouts over eggs.

Tilt pan and roll up edges of omelette, or simply fold omelette in half. Slide onto serving plate. (This whole procedure should take about 1 minute.) Serve immediately. Makes 2 servings.

Calories per serving: 221
Grams fat per serving: 16
Vitamin A: Excellent
Iron, riboflavin, phosphorus and niacin: Good

A 2 egg omelette is easier to make than a 4 egg or larger omelette. Also, it's important to use the correct size of pan. For a 2 to 3 egg omelette, use an omelette pan 7 inches/18 cm in diameter at the bottom; for a 4 egg omelette, use an 8 to 9 inch/ 20 to 23 cm pan.

Egg yolks are high in cholesterol—so do remember to limit your consumption.

BULGUR WHEAT, TOFU AND SWEET PEPPERS

*See page 64 for information on bulgur wheat.

Tofu

It's cheap, nutritious, low in calories and fat. Tofu or soy-bean curd is one of the best sources of non-animal (vegetable) protein you can find, as well as being rich in calcium, phosphorus and iron.

Tofu is usually sold in a cus-tard-like cake form, covered in water, packed either in 1 lb/450 g plastic tubs or vacuum-packs. Check the "Use by" date to make sure it is fresh.

Store tofu in the refrigerator and change the water it is packaged in every day. It will stay fresh for up to 7 days.

Tofu has a mild taste and can be used in everything from appetizers to desserts. Cut it into cubes and add it to soups or salads. Mash it and season with fresh herbs or spices, mustard or garlic; add a little yogurt or sour cream and serve as a dip or sauce.

This main course vegetarian dish is a good source of protein and fibre. If possible, use bulgur instead of cracked wheat; it has a nuttier, richer flavour and takes less time to cook.

6 oz	coarse or medium bulgur or cracked wheat*	175 g
1 oz	butter	25 g
3	garlic cloves, chopped	3
2 tsp	ground cumin	10 ml
2	sweet red peppers, seeded and cut in strips	2
3 tbsp	vinegar	45 ml
5 tbsp	water	75 ml
10 oz	fresh spinach, washed, stemmed and cut in strips	300 g
1 tsp	salt	5 ml
	Freshly ground pepper	
12 oz	firm-style tofu or bean curd, cut in cubes	350 g

Rinse bulgur under cold water. Place in bowl and add enough cold water to cover by 2 inches/5 cm; soak for 1 hour. Drain thoroughly in sieve.

In large frying pan, melt butter over medium heat, add garlic and cook for a few seconds. Stir in cumin, then peppers. Cover and cook for 5 minutes.

Add bulgur, vinegar and water; cook, uncovered, for 5 minutes or until bulgur is nearly tender, stirring often (cracked wheat will take about 15 minutes longer; add more water as necessary). Add spinach; stir until mixed and spinach is slightly wilted. Season with salt and pepper to taste. Add tofu; cover and simmer for 5 minutes or until heated through and flavours are blended. Makes 6 main course servings.

Calories per serving: 252
Grams fat per serving: 7
Fibre: Excellent
Vitamins A and C and iron: Excellent
Niacin and phosphorus: Good

FETTUCCINE WITH FRESH TOMATOES AND BASIL

Easy Summer Supper
Fettuccine with Fresh Tomatoes and Basil (page 137)
Tossed Green Salad with Blue Cheese Dressing (page 84)
Sliced fresh peaches

This is a delightful supper in late summer or autumn when tomatoes are at their best. For the most fibre, try to buy wholewheat noodles.

6 oz	fettuccine noodles	175 g
2 tbsp	olive oil	30 ml
2	garlic cloves, chopped	2
4	tomatoes, diced	4
$\frac{1}{2}$ tsp	dried basil or 2 tbsp/30 ml chopped fresh	2 ml
Pinch	granulated sugar	Pinch
4 tbsp	chopped fresh parsley	60 ml
	Salt and freshly ground pepper	
2 tbsp	grated Parmesan cheese	30 ml

In large pot of boiling salted water, cook noodles until al dente (tender but firm). Meanwhile, in heavy frying pan, heat oil over medium heat; stir in garlic, tomatoes, basil and sugar and cook for 5 minutes, stirring occasionally. Add parsley, and salt and pepper to taste.

Drain noodles. Toss with tomato mixture and Parmesan. (If sauce is too thick, add a few spoonfuls of pasta cooking liquid.) Serve with extra Parmesan. Makes 2 main course servings, 4 appetizer or side dish servings.

Calories per main course serving: 425
Grams fat per main course serving: 14
Fibre: Good
Vitamins A and C, thiamin and niacin: Excellent
Calcium, riboflavin, phosphorus and iron: Good

CREAMY PASTA WITH BROCCOLI, CAULIFLOWER AND MUSHROOMS

Here's a hearty pasta dish your family will love. The variety of vegetables you can use is limitless—try adding carrots, mangetout, celery or green beans.

1	small head cauliflower, trimmed and cut in florets	1
1	small bunch broccoli, trimmed and cut in florets	1
	Salt	
2 tbsp	olive oil or vegetable oil	30 ml
3	garlic cloves, chopped	3
10 oz	mushrooms, thickly sliced	300 g
4 oz	wholewheat noodles (or egg noodles or spaghettini)	125 g
8 oz	cottage cheese	250 ml
4 fl oz	milk	125 ml
4 tbsp	sour cream	60 ml
4 tbsp	grated Parmesan cheese	60 ml
	Salt and cayenne pepper	

In large pot of boiling salted water, cook cauliflower and broccoli until tender crisp, about 5 minutes. With slotted spoon, remove vegetables and save the liquid for cooking the pasta.

In large frying pan, heat oil; sauté garlic for 2 minutes over medium heat; add mushrooms and sauté for about 5 minutes. Stir in broccoli and cauliflower; sauté for 2 to 3 minutes longer. Set aside.

Meanwhile, in reserved boiling vegetable liquid, cook pasta, adding water if necessary, until al dente (tender but firm), about 8 to 10 minutes; drain.

In food processor, combine cottage cheese, milk, sour cream and Parmesan. Pour over broccoli mixture; add drained pasta and toss until mixed. Season with salt and cayenne pepper to taste. Serve immediately. Makes about 8 servings.

Calories per serving: 301
Grams fat per serving: 5
Fibre: Excellent
Vitamins A and C: Excellent
Thiamin, niacin, phosphorus and iron: Good

DEEP-DISH VEGETABLE PIZZA

This scrumptious pizza is very filling. Two slices are plenty for dinner along with a salad.

*This method makes a thick crust. If you want a thin crust, divide dough into three portions and use the extra dough to make another pizza base. Dough can be frozen.

	Wholewheat Pizza Dough (page 178)	
8 fl oz	tomato sauce or chopped tomatoes	250 ml
1 tbsp	garlic, finely chopped	15 ml
1 tsp	each oregano and basil	5 ml
1 tsp	oil	5 ml
3	onions, sliced	3
8 oz	mushrooms, sliced	225 g
	Salt and freshly ground pepper	
1 lb	broccoli, 1 inch/2.5 cm pieces	450 g
1 lb	grated mozzarella cheese	450 g

Prepare pizza dough. Divide dough into 2 pieces.* Roll out each piece to fit an 8 to 9 inch/20 to 23 cm round quiche or cake tin that's at least 1½ inches/4 cm deep.

In small bowl, combine tomato sauce, garlic, oregano and basil; stir to mix.

In heavy frying pan, heat oil over medium heat; add onions and cook over medium to low heat, stirring until tender, 5 to 10 minutes.

Add mushrooms and cook over medium heat, stirring or shaking pan until mushrooms are lightly browned and liquid has evaporated. Sprinkle with salt and pepper to taste and set aside.

In large pot of boiling water, cook broccoli for 2 minutes or until bright green; drain and cool under cold running water to prevent any further cooking. Drain again and set aside.

Spread tomato mixture over dough in pans. Cover with broccoli, then with mushroom and onion mixture. Sprinkle with grated cheese. Bake in 425°F/220°C/Gas Mark 7 oven for 30 to 40 minutes or until crust is browned and top is bubbly. Makes 2 pizzas.

Calories per ¼ pizza: 293
Grams fat per ¼ pizza: 14
Fibre: Excellent
Vitamins A and C, riboflavin, niacin, phosphorus, thiamin and calcium: Excellent
Iron: Good

TRIPLE CHEESE LASAGNE

If making this for a special occasion, add sliced mushrooms and chopped sweet green or red pepper to the tomato sauce. No one will notice it doesn't have meat.

1	can (14 oz/400 g) tomatoes, undrained	1
1	jar (14 oz/400 g) tomato sauce	1
2	onions, chopped	2
2	garlic cloves, chopped	2
2 tbsp	chopped parsley	30 ml
2 tsp	granulated sugar	10 ml
1 tsp	basil leaves	5 ml
1 tsp	thyme	5 ml
1 tsp	Salt	15 ml
	Freshly ground pepper	
8 oz	lasagne	225 g
3 oz	grated Parmesan cheese	75 g
1 lb	cottage cheese	450 g
1	egg, lightly beaten	1
1 tsp	oregano	5 ml
8 oz	grated mozzarella cheese	225 g

In saucepan, combine tomatoes, tomato sauce, onions, garlic, parsley, sugar, basil, thyme, 1 tsp/5 ml of the salt, and pepper to taste. Bring to a boil. Reduce heat and simmer, uncovered, stirring occasionally, for 30 minutes or until mixture has a spaghetti sauce consistency.

In large pot of boiling water, cook lasagne noodles until al dente (tender but firm). Drain and rinse under cold running water; drain well.

Reserve 3 tbsp/45 ml of the Parmesan cheese for topping. In bowl, combine remaining Parmesan cheese, cottage cheese, egg, oregano, 1 tsp/5 ml salt, and pepper to taste. Mix well and set aside.

Reserve 4 fl oz/125 ml of the tomato sauce for topping. In 13 × 9-inch/3.5 L baking dish, spoon just enough of the tomato sauce to cover bottom sparingly; top with a layer of lasagne noodles. Cover with $\frac{1}{3}$ of the cottage cheese mixture, then $\frac{1}{3}$ of the mozzarella cheese. Repeat with remaining sauce, noodles and cheeses to make 3 layers of each.

Top with reserved tomato sauce and sprinkle with reserved Parmesan cheese. Bake, uncovered, in 350°F/180°C/Gas Mark 4 oven for 45 minutes or until hot and bubbly. Remove from oven and let cool slightly before serving. Makes 8 servings.

Calories per serving: 210
Grams fat per serving: 6
Niacin: Excellent
Vitamins A and C, calcium and phosphorus: Good

WINTER VEGETABLE STEW

Other vegetables can be added to or substituted for the vegetables suggested here. Broccoli, green beans, asparagus in season, mangetout or other quick cooking vegetables can be added to the stew when you add the courgettes.

2 tbsp	vegetable oil	30 ml
4	onions, coarsely chopped	4
4	large garlic cloves, chopped	4
3 or 4	leeks	3 or 4
4	potatoes	4
4	carrots	4
$\frac{1}{2}$	small swede	$\frac{1}{2}$
1	sweet potato (optional)	1
2 pts	water (preferably vegetable cooking water) or chicken stock	1.25 L
2 tsp	crumbled oregano leaves	10 ml
2 tsp	crumbled thyme leaves	10 ml
2	small unpeeled courgettes, cut in chunks	2
	Salt and freshly ground pepper	
	Chopped fresh parsley	
	Grated Parmesan cheese	

In large heavy saucepan, heat oil over medium heat. Add onions and garlic; cook until tender.

Discard tough green parts of leeks; cut leeks in half lengthwise and wash under cold running water. Cut into $\frac{3}{4}$ inch/2 cm pieces. Peel potatoes, carrots, swede and sweet potato; cut into 1 inch/2.5 cm cubes.

Add vegetables to saucepan as they are prepared. Stir in water, oregano and thyme; bring to a boil. Cover and simmer until vegetables are tender, about 30 minutes. Stir in courgette, and salt and pepper to taste; simmer for 5 minutes or until all vegetables are tender, adding more water if desired.

Ladle stew into bowls and sprinkle with parsley. Serve Parmesan cheese separately to sprinkle over stew. Makes 6 main course servings.

Calories per serving without Parmesan: 205
Grams fat per serving without Parmesan: 4.8
Calories including 1 tbsp/15 ml Parmesan per serving: 237
Grams fat including 1 tbsp/15 ml Parmesan per serving: 6.3
Fibre: Excellent
Vitamins A and C, and niacin: Excellent
Phosphorus: Good

BAKED COURGETTE OMELETTE

Similar to a crustless courgette and spinach quiche or a frittata, this is ideal with toast and salad or sliced tomatoes for lunch or dinner.

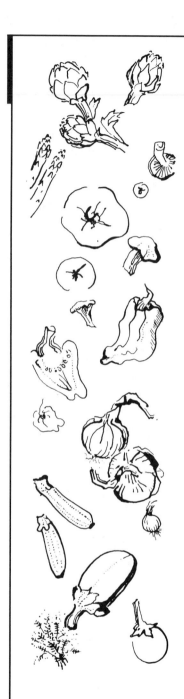

½ oz	butter	15 g
1	onion, chopped	1
1	garlic clove, chopped	1
8 oz	thinly sliced unpeeled courgette	225 g
2 oz	grated low-fat cheese	50 g
2 tbsp	chopped fresh parsley	30 ml
5	eggs, lightly beaten	5
10 oz	pkt frozen chopped spinach, thawed and drained	300 g
1 tsp	salt	5 ml
	Freshly ground pepper	

In heavy frying pan, melt butter over medium heat; cook onion and garlic until onion is tender. Add courgette and cook, stirring for 5 minutes.

In bowl, combine parsley, cheese, eggs, spinach, salt, and pepper to taste; mix well. Stir in courgette mixture. Spoon into lightly oiled 9 inch/23 cm pie plate. Bake in 325°F/160°C/Gas Mark 3 oven for 35 to 45 minutes or until set but still moist. Serve hot or cold. Makes 4 main course servings.

Calories per serving: 154
Grams fat per serving: 9
Fibre: Excellent
Vitamins A and C: Excellent
Iron and niacin: Good

TUSCAN WHITE KIDNEY BEAN AND TOMATO CASSEROLE

Tomato Consommé
In large saucepan, combine 12 fl oz/375 ml tomato juice, 1 10 oz/284 ml can consommé or beef bouillon, 8 fl oz/250 ml water, ½ tsp/2 ml basil and 1 tbsp/15 ml lemon juice. Bring to a boil. Reduce heat and simmer 1 to 2 minutes. Remove from heat and add 2 tbsp/30 ml sherry or white wine (or to taste) and some freshly ground pepper. Ladle into mugs and garnish with thinly sliced lemon. Serve hot. Makes 5 servings.

You'll want to have a little of this left over—it's delicious cold. Good as a main course with a green salad and wholewheat pitta bread, it's a high fibre dinner that's easy to make.

1 tbsp	vegetable oil	15 ml
1	onion, thinly sliced	1
1	garlic clove, chopped	1
1	large tomato, seeded and coarsely choped	1
1	small sweet green pepper, diced	1
¼ tsp	basil	1 ml
Pinch	oregano	Pinch
1	can (15.2 oz/432 g) white kidney beans, drained	1
	Salt and freshly ground pepper	
1 oz	chopped fresh parsley	25 g

In small heavy saucepan or flameproof casserole, heat oil over medium heat. Add onion and cook until tender. Stir in garlic, tomato and green pepper; cook for 1 minute. Stir in basil, oregano, kidney beans, and salt and pepper to taste. Simmer over low heat for 5 minutes or until heated through and flavours are blended. Stir in parsley. Makes 2 main course servings.

Calories per serving: 243
Grams fat per serving: 7
Fibre: Excellent
Iron and vitamins A and C: Excellent
Phosphorus, thiamin and niacin: Good

SAUCES

For two years I was a national judge for Wiser's Deluxe Culinary Competition in Montreal. Most of the other judges were very experienced, award-winning chefs. It was here that I learned that the real test of a chef is his or her sauces. The judges would quickly decide how well meat was cooked, arranged and garnished, but the sauce for the meat would be tasted and discussed at great length. It had to be silky smooth, full of flavour but not overpowering, not too thick but not watery either. The sauces we tasted were exquisite, made from long-simmering stocks and enriched with butter and cream.

Now health conscious diners are demanding lower calorie sauces, and, as a result, a whole new collection of sauces is in vogue. Light-lean or alternative cuisines are part of expense-account restaurant menus with exciting, innovative dishes. Red peppers are slowly roasted, then puréed, to blanket a plate for tender, juicy chicken breasts. Sun-ripened mangoes, puréed with lemon or lime juice, complement perfectly cooked fish.

Most home cooks don't have wonderful homemade stock bases on hand. We want tasty sauces we can make in five to ten minutes. We want light sauces that are not loaded with calories, cholesterol and fat. Here is a selection of sauces that will fool even the most serious diners. They're full of flavour, yet low in fat, especially when compared to traditional sauces. And most are very quick to prepare.

Diet Hint: Reducing fat content in sauces

- To remove fat from pan juices, skim surface fat or throw in ice cubes. Fat will adhere to the ice and can be easily removed. Or, pour juices into a container and put in freezer. Remove solid fat from the surface. To thicken cold juices, add 2 tbsp/30 ml flour per 8 fl oz/250 ml of juice and heat, stirring until thickened and smooth.

- Boil down pan juices if they're too thin.
- If using homemade beef or chicken stock, refrigerate or freeze just before using. The fat will solidify on top and lift off easily.
- Use yogurt or puréed cottage cheese as a base for cold, cream type sauces, instead of cream or mayonnaise.
- Instead of whipped cream, use fruits such as strawberries or raspberries puréed in a

food processor or blender. These make delicious sauces to serve with other fruits, ice creams, sherbets or cakes, and they are low in fat and calories.
- Many desserts are too sweet and need whipped cream or crème fraîche to tone down the sweetness. You won't need the whipped cream if you reduce the amount of sugar in puddings, pies and fruit desserts instead.

*Fresh dill gives this sauce
excellent flavour; if not
available, substitute 2 tbps/30 ml
chopped fresh parsley and
1 tsp/5 ml dried dill. You can
also make this sauce using all
yogurt or all cottage cheese.

BRAMBLE SAUCE

This sauce is delicious with turkey, chicken and ham. Conventional gravy is much higher in fat than this sweet, yet tart, sauce. Currant jelly can be used instead of bramble.

8 oz	bramble jelly (blackberry)	225 ml
3 tbsp	orange juice	45 ml
1 tsp	grated orange rind (or grated rind of $\frac{1}{2}$ orange)	5 ml
5 tbsp	brandy	75 ml
4 tbsp	red wine vinegar or balsamic vinegar	60 ml

In small saucepan, combine jelly, orange juice, brandy and vinegar. Heat over low heat until jelly is melted; stir well. Makes 16 fl oz/500 ml sauce.

Calories per 1 tbsp/15 ml: 30
Grams fat per 1 tbsp/15 ml: 0

DILL MUSTARD SAUCE

Serve with hot or cold dishes and seafood, as a dressing for salads, or with chicken or turkey, or toss with cold cooked pasta.

5 tbsp	plain yogurt	75 ml
5 tbsp	cottage cheese	75 ml
2 tbsp	chopped fresh dill*	30 ml
$1\frac{1}{2}$ tsp	Dijon mustard	7 ml

In food processor or blender, combine yogurt, cottage cheese, dill and mustard; process until smooth. Alternatively, pass cottage cheese through a sieve, then mix with remaining ingredients. Makes 6 fl oz/175 ml sauce.

Calories per 1 tbsp/15 ml: 11
Grams fat per 1 tbsp/15 ml: 0.1

CREAMY HERB SAUCE

Fresh herbs add wonderful flavour to sauces. Creamy Fresh Dill Dip (page 30) is delicious as a sauce and low in fat as well. Instead of fresh dill, substitute 1 to 2 tbsp/15 to 30 ml of chopped fresh tarragon, basil or a combination of whatever fresh herbs you have on hand.

Calories per 1 tbsp/15 ml: 12
Grams fat per 1 tbsp/15 ml: 0.3

Ways To Cut Fat

SAUCE FOR	INSTEAD OF	Grams fat per 2 tbsp/30 ml	CHOOSE	Grams fat per 2 tbsp/30 ml
Asparagus, broccoli Fish and eggs Benedict	Conventional Hollandaise	7.8+	Yogurt Hollandaise (pages 150–1)	1.8
Pork	Homemade gravy	5.9	Cinnamon Apple Sauce (page 219)	0.2
			Red Pepper Purée (pages 154–5)	1.5
Beef	Homemade gravy	5.9	Pan juices (fat removed)	0.15
Steak	Béarnaise sauce	7.2+	Tarragon and Mushroom Sauce (page 150)	1.4
Chicken and turkey	Homemade gravy	5.9	Pan juices (fat removed)	0.15
			Cranberry Sauce or Bramble Sauce (page 147)	0.5
Hot or cold poached salmon and other fish	Cream sauces: thick (white sauce) medium thin	3.6 3.1 2.6	Creamy Herb Sauce (page 148)	0.5
	Mayonnaise	24	Dill Mustard Sauce (page 147)	0.2
Pasta	Butter and cream based sauces	10+	Tomato and Basil Sauce (page 149)	0
	Conventional pesto recipe	7	Pesto (page 46)	3

TOMATO AND BASIL SAUCE

Use this sauce over spaghetti, macaroni or other pasta, as a base for pizza or with cooked vegetables such as courgette or green beans. Use the dried leaf form of basil and oregano if you can find them, not ground; crush the herbs by rubbing them between the palms of your hands before adding to the sauce.

2	cans (each 14 oz/400 g) plum tomatoes, undrained	2
5 oz	tomato purée	150 g
2	onions, finely chopped	2
2	garlic cloves, chopped	2
1	large bay leaf	1
2 tbsp	crumbled basil	30 ml
2 tsp	crumbled leaf oregano	10 ml
1 tsp	salt	5 ml
	Freshly ground pepper, sugar	

In food processor, purée tomatoes. Pour into large, heavy saucepan and add tomato purée, onions, garlic, bay leaf, basil and oregano. Simmer, uncovered, for 20 to 30 minutes or until sauce has thickened slightly and onions are tender. (If sauce thickens too quickly, cover for remaining cooking time.) Add salt, and pepper and sugar to taste. Makes about 2½ pts/1.5 L sauce.

Calories per 4 fl oz/125 ml: 38
Grams fat per 4 fl oz/125 ml: 0.3
Vitamins A and C: Excellent

TARRAGON AND MUSHROOM SAUCE

Similar in taste to Béarnaise sauce but with much less butter, this is delicious served warm with steak, meatballs, lentil burgers and other meats.

½ oz	butter	15 g
4 oz	mushrooms, chopped	125 g
1	chopped spring onion	1
4 tsp	plain flour	20 ml
½ tsp	dried tarragon	2 ml
16 fl oz	beef stock	500 ml

In small saucepan, melt butter over medium heat. Add mushrooms and onion and cook, stirring occasionally, until tender and most of the liquid has evaporated. Sprinkle with flour and tarragon; cook, stirring, for 2 minutes.

Bring stock to a boil; gradually pour into mushroom mixture while whisking constantly. Cook, stirring constantly, until mixture thickens slightly and boils. Simmer, uncovered, for 10 to 20 minutes or until sauce is reduced to about 8 fl oz/250 ml. Serve hot. Makes 8 fl oz/250 ml.

Calories per 1 tbsp/15 ml: 10
Grams fat per 1 tbsp/15 ml: 0.7

YOGURT HOLLANDAISE

Use this sauce with vegetables or fish. It is like a Hollandaise in taste but is made with yogurt instead of butter.

8 fl oz	plain yogurt	250 ml
2 tsp	lemon juice	10 ml
3	egg yolks	3
½ tsp	salt	2 ml
½ tsp	Dijon mustard	2 ml
Pinch	freshly ground pepper	Pinch
1 tbsp	chopped fresh dill or parsley (optional)	15 ml

*Egg yolk mixtures cooked in an aluminium pan will discolour

For other sauce recipes, see:
Red Pepper Purée
(pages 154–5)
Curry Sauce (page 171)
Pesto (pages 46–7)

For dessert sauces,
see pages 219–21

In top of non-aluminium double boiler or saucepan,* beat yogurt, lemon juice and egg yolks. Heat over simmering water, stirring frequently, until sauce has thickened, about 15 minutes. (Sauce will become thinner after about 10 minutes of cooking, then will thicken again.) Remove from heat and stir in salt, mustard, pepper and dill (if using). Serve warm. (Sauce can be prepared in advance, refrigerated for up to 1 week, then reheated over hot, not simmering, water.) Makes about 12 fl oz/300 ml.

Calories per 1 tbsp/15 ml: 17
Grams fat per 1 tbsp/15 ml: 0.9

TOMATO SALSA

Serve this Mexican staple on lettuce or as a topping for tacos or over cottage cheese, as a dip with endive wedges, as a filling for pitta bread or as an accompaniment to meats.

4	large tomatoes, peeled, seeded and diced	4
1	large sweet green pepper, seeded and diced	1
1	fresh hot chilli pepper or 1 or 2 canned green chilli peppers, seeded and diced	1
1 tbsp	grated onion	15 ml
1	small garlic clove, crushed	1
2 tbsp	chopped coriander leaves	30 ml
1 tsp	crumbled leaf oregano	5 ml
	Salt and freshly ground pepper	

In bowl, combine tomatoes, green pepper, chilli pepper, onion, garlic, coriander and oregano; mix well. Season with salt and pepper to taste. Cover and refrigerate until needed. Makes 8 servings (4 fl oz/125 ml each).

Calories per serving: 27
Grams fat per serving: 0.2
Vitamins A and C: Excellent

VEGETABLES

always look forward to the change in seasons, not because of the weather, but for the new vegetables it brings to the table. What could possibly taste better than the first bite of June's tender asparagus, July's juicy tomatoes full of sun-sweetened flavour or your first feed of locally grown, sweet and juicy corn-on-the-cob in August? I enjoy the vegetables as much as, if not more than, the meat portion of a meal.

Not only are vegetables delicious, they also play an important role in a healthy diet. Many vegetables are good sources of fibre, vitamins (especially A and C) and minerals, as well as being low in fat and calories. It's the butter, oil and cream you serve with vegetables that add the fat and calories, not the vegetables themselves.

Eating three or more servings a day of a variety of vegetables will help you meet the World Cancer Research Fund's Dietary Guidelines. A daily intake of at least three vegetables will help you meet their recommendations for fibre, vitamin C and carotene (which is converted to vitamin A in the body). At the same time, as long as you don't add extra butter or other fats, vegetables will help you maintain your ideal weight and restrict your total fat intake to no more than 30 per cent of your daily calorie intake.

When planning meals, include both fresh and raw vegetables. Make sure you have a pleasing combination of colours, flavours and textures. For instance, don't serve turnip, cauliflower and parsnip at the same meal. They're all strongly flavoured, similar in texture and lacking in colour contrast. Include bright green, deep-yellow and orange vegetables as much as possible, not only for their visual appeal but for their nutrients.

For the most fibre and vitamins
- Don't peel vegetables if the skins are edible (e.g., potatoes, courgettes, cucumber). They contain fibre as well as nutrients.
- Don't discard the seeds if they're edible (e.g., those in tomatoes and cucumbers). They are excellent sources of fibre.
- Don't overcook vegetables.
- Eat vegetables raw as often as possible.
- Refer to Table G (page 236) to see which vegetables have the most fibre.

Opposite:
Scallops and Prawns in Wine
Bouillon with Julienne
Vegetables (page 124)

TOMATOES FLORENTINE

These are an attractive make-ahead addition to a buffet table or dinner.

6	tomatoes	6
½ oz	butter	15 g
1	small onion, finely chopped	1
1	garlic clove, chopped	1
12 oz	pkt frozen chopped spinach, thawed and drained	350 g
5 tbsp	milk	75 ml
	Salt and freshly ground pepper	
Topping		
2 tbsp	fine dry bread crumbs	30 ml
2 tbsp	chopped fresh parsley	30 ml
2 tsp	grated Parmesan cheese	10 ml

Cut a slice from top of each tomato. Scoop out pulp to halfway down tomato and save for sauce or soup.

In frying pan, melt butter. Stir in onion and garlic; cook over medium heat until tender. Stir in spinach, milk, and salt and pepper to taste. Spoon mixture into tomatoes and arrange in ovenproof serving dish or on baking sheet.

Topping: Combine bread crumbs, parsley and cheese; sprinkle over top of tomatoes. Bake in 400°F/200°C/Gas Mark 6 oven for 20 minutes or until heated through. Makes 6 servings.

Calories per serving: 70
Grams fat per serving: 2
Fibre: Excellent
Vitamins A and C: Excellent
Folacin: Good

Variation
Tomatoes Provençal: Cut 6 tomatoes in half crosswise. Combine 2 oz/50 g fine bread crumbs, 1 large clove chopped garlic, 4 tbsp/60 ml chopped parsley and 1 tbsp/15 ml olive oil. Sprinkle crumb mixture over tomato halves and place on baking sheet. Bake in 400°F/200°C/Gas Mark 6 oven for 15 minutes or until heated through. Makes 6 servings.

Opposite:
Deep-Dish Vegetable Pizza
(page 139)

GLAZED BRUSSELS SPROUTS WITH PECANS

Traditional with a turkey dinner, this recipe can be easily doubled or tripled. Walnuts can be used instead of pecans. Just make sure they are fresh.

8 oz	small Brussels sprouts	225 g
½ oz	butter	15 g
2 tsp	granulated sugar	10 ml
2 tbsp	coarsely chopped pecans	30 ml
	Salt and freshly ground pepper	

Trim base of sprouts and outside leaves. Steam sprouts over boiling water for about 10 minutes or until tender. Drain thoroughly.

In frying pan, melt butter over medium heat; add sugar and stir until melted. Add sprouts and pecans; stir to coat well and cook for 1 to 2 minutes. Season with salt and pepper to taste. Makes 4 servings.

Calories per serving: 81
Grams fat per serving: 5
Fibre: Good
Vitamin C: Excellent

ASPARAGUS WITH RED PEPPER PURÉE

Serve this colourful dish as a first course in asparagus season.

2	large sweet red peppers	2
2 tsp	olive oil	10 ml
¼ tsp	dried thyme	1 ml
	Freshly ground pepper	
2 lb	asparagus	1 kg

Roast peppers on a baking sheet in 375°F/190°C/Gas Mark 5 oven for 18 minutes. Turn and roast on other side for 18 minutes longer or until peppers are blistered and soft. Remove from oven and place hot peppers in a heavy paper

Brussels sprouts belong to the brassica genus of the cruciferous family of vegetables. People whose diets frequently include these vegetables have a lower risk of colon cancer.

Spring Dinner Party Menu
Asparagus with Red Pepper Purée (page 154–5)
Marinated Leg of Lamb with Coriander (pages 114–15)
Cracked Wheat and Basil Pilaf (page 173)
Steamed cherry tomatoes and mangetout or Sautéed Courgette with Yogurt and Herbs (page 163) or Stir-fried Vegetables with Ginger and Garlic (pages 166–7)
Fresh Strawberry Sorbet (page 193)

Roasted red peppers have a wonderful rich flavour. They're usually quickly roasted under a grill, over a flame or on the barbecue until they char and blacken. We recommend roasting them slowly just until they blister, not until they char, since charred or barbecued food may contain carcinogenic substances.

or plastic bag. Close bag and let peppers steam for 10 to 15 minutes. Using fingers and a small knife, peel skin from peppers (it should come off easily); seed peppers and cut into strips.

In frying pan, heat oil over medium heat; when hot, add roasted peppers and thyme. Sauté for 2 minutes; season with pepper to taste. Purée in food processor. (Purée can be prepared in advance, covered and refrigerated for up to 1 week; reheat gently over low heat before continuing with recipe.)

Wash and break tough ends off asparagus; cook in large pot of boiling water for 5 to 8 minutes or until tender; drain thoroughly.

Spoon hot pepper purée over individual plates. Arrange hot asparagus on top. Makes 6 servings.

Calories per serving: 56
Grams fat per serving: 2.6
Fibre: Good
Vitamins A and C: Excellent

TARRAGON CARROTS

Onion and tarragon go well with the sweetness of carrots. Cook them in the oven or microwave to retain the vitamins, and save time by slicing the carrots and onions in the food processor.

4	large carrots, thinly sliced	4
2	small onions, thinly sliced	2
1 tsp	tarragon	5 ml
2 tbsp	water	30 ml
	Salt and freshly ground pepper	
2 tsp	butter	10 ml

Lightly oil a large sheet of foil or a 2½ pt/1.5 L microwave dish. On foil or in dish, place carrots and onion; sprinkle with tarragon, water, and salt and pepper to taste. Wrap tightly or cover. Cook in 350°F/180°C/Gas Mark 4 oven for 30 minutes, or microwave on High for 10 to 12 minutes, or until tender. Stir in butter. Makes 4 servings.

Calories per serving: 37
Grams fat per serving: 2
Fibre: Good
Vitamin A: Excellent

Lemon and Ginger Carrots
Combine 1tbsp/15 ml each butter, granulated sugar and lemon juice with 1 tsp/5 ml each of grated lemon rind and grated fresh ginger root; cook until sugar dissolves. Toss with 4–6 large sliced hot carrots.

Add butter at the end of the cooking of vegetables to get maximum flavour with minimum fat.

BROCCOLI AND SWEET PEPPER STIR-FRY

This colourful red, yellow and green vegetable dish tastes as good as it looks.

1	bunch broccoli (about 1 lb/450 g)	1
1	sweet red pepper	1
1	sweet yellow pepper	1
1 tbsp	vegetable oil	15 ml
1	onion, chopped	1
1 tsp	grated fresh ginger root	5 ml
4 tbsp	chicken stock	60 ml
2 tsp	low-sodium soy sauce	10 ml

Peel tough broccoli stems. Cut stems and florets into pieces about 1½ inches/4 cm long. Blanch in large pot of boiling water for 2 to 3 minutes or until bright green and tender crisp; drain, cool under cold running water and dry on paper towels. Seed peppers and cut into thin strips. (This can be done in advance.)

In large heavy frying pan or wok, heat oil over medium heat. Add onion and ginger; stir-fry for 1 minute. Add peppers and stir-fry for 2 to 3 minutes, adding chicken stock when necessary to prevent sticking or scorching. Add broccoli; stir-fry until heated through; sprinkle with soy sauce. Serve immediately. Makes 8 servings.

Calories per serving: 40
Grams fat per serving: 2
Fibre: Good
Vitamins A and C: Excellent

BRAISED RED CABBAGE

Eating cabbage and other brassica vegetables may reduce the risk of cancer of the colon.

Here's a vegetable that's especially good with pork or poultry. You can make this a day or two in advance and reheat it. To retain a bright red colour when cooking red cabbage, include an acid such as vinegar or lemon juice in the cooking liquid.

$\frac{1}{2}$	medium red cabbage	$\frac{1}{2}$
1	cooking apple	1
5 tbsp	water	75 ml
4 tbsp	white wine vinegar	60 ml
	Salt and freshly ground pepper	
2 tbsp	(approx) honey or granulated sugar	30 ml

Remove outer leaves and centre core of cabbage. Slice thinly. Peel, core and slice apple. In large frying pan or heavy pan, combine cabbage, apple, water and vinegar. Stir and bring to a boil. Reduce heat and simmer, covered, stirring occasionally, for 1 hour or until cabbage is very tender.

Stir in salt, pepper and honey to taste. The flavour should be sweet and sour. Adjust seasoning if necessary. Makes 4 servings.

Calories per serving: 55
Grams fat per serving: 0.3
Fibre: Good
Vitamin C: Excellent

Excellent Sources of Fibre
(more than 4 grams of fibre per serving)
3½ oz/100 g Red Kidney Beans
3½ oz/100 g Green Peas
3½ oz/100 g Blackeyed Beans
3½ oz/100 g Broccoli
3½ oz/100 g Spinach
5 oz/150 g Baked Beans
3½ oz/100 g Chick Peas

Good Sources of Fibre
(2 to 3.9 grams fibre per serving)
3½ oz/100 g Beetroot
3½ oz/100 g Cabbage
3½ oz/100 g Parsnips
4 oz/125 g Lentils
4 Brussels Sprouts
3½ oz/100 g Carrots
3½ oz/100 g Sweetcorn
(Measurements are for cooked vegetables)

The Mysterious Ingredient
Several studies have indicated that vegetables from the cabbage family, or brassica genus (of the cruciferous family), may reduce the risk of cancer of the colon. Something in these vegetables may help block formation of this cancer in the body.

The brassica vegetables include: cabbage, broccoli, cauliflower, Brussels sprouts, swede, kale, turnip.

SCALLOPED CABBAGE AU GRATIN

Here's a good way to serve cabbage. It's a delicious dish that adds some protein to a meatless meal, and also goes well with hot or cold beef, pork and lamb. The dish may be prepared in advance and baked just before serving.

2 lb	coarsely shredded cabbage	900 g
1	can (14 oz/400 g) tomatoes, undrained	1
2 tsp	granulated sugar	10 ml
$\frac{1}{4}$ tsp	paprika	1 ml
1 tsp	salt	5 ml
1 tsp	oregano	5 ml
	Salt and freshly ground pepper	
2 oz	grated Cheddar cheese	50 g
3 oz	fine fresh bread crumbs	75 g

Cook cabbage in boiling salted water until wilted, about 6 minutes; drain well. Combine tomatoes, sugar, paprika, salt and oregano, breaking up tomatoes with back of spoon. In greased 2$\frac{1}{2}$ pt/1.5 L baking dish, place cabbage. Sprinkle with salt and pepper to taste. Cover with tomato mixture, then cheese. Top with crumbs. Bake, uncovered in 350°F/180°C/Gas Mark 4 oven for 30 minutes or until heated through. Makes 6 servings.

Calories per serving: 133
Grams fat per serving: 7
Fibre: Good
Vitamin C: Excellent
Calcium and vitamin A: Good

TWO CABBAGE STIR-FRY

Autumn Dinner Menu
Pork Tenderloin with Rosemary
and Thyme (page 111)
Two Cabbage Stir-Fry (page 159)
Mashed Potatoes with Onions
(page 170) and/or green peas
Peach Blackcurrant Crisp
(page 208)

Red and green cabbage stir-fried with ginger and onion is a delicious vegetable dish that's especially good with pork and turkey. Rice vinegar is a mild, sweet vinegar, available in the Chinese food section of many supermarkets. (Recipe can be doubled.)

1 tbsp	rice vinegar	15 ml
1 tbsp	water	15 ml
1 tsp	low-sodium soy sauce	5 ml
1 tsp	cornflour	5 ml
1 tbsp	vegetable oil	15 ml
1 tsp	chopped fresh ginger root	5 ml
1	small onion, chopped	1
8 oz	thinly sliced red cabbage	225 g
8 oz	thinly sliced green cabbage	225 g

In small dish, mix together vinegar, water, soy sauce and cornflour; set aside.

In wok or heavy frying pan, heat oil over medium heat. Add ginger and onion; stir-fry for 1 minute. Add both kinds of cabbage and stir-fry until tender, 3 to 5 minutes.

Pour in soy sauce mixture and stir-fry until liquid comes to a boil, about 1 minute. Serve hot. Makes 3 servings.

Calories per serving: 75
Grams fat per serving: 5
Fibre: Good
Vitamin C: Excellent

HERBED GREEN BEANS WITH GARLIC

Herbs, onion and garlic enhance the flavour of beans without adding calories or fat.

1 lb	green beans	450 g
2 tsp	oil	10 ml
1	small onion, thinly sliced	1
1	garlic clove, chopped	1
1 tbsp	chopped fresh thyme or oregano (or $\frac{1}{2}$ tsp/2 ml dried)	15 ml
	Salt and freshly ground pepper	

Trim beans and cook in rapidly boiling water for 4 to 5 minutes or until tender crisp; drain.

In heavy frying pan or saucepan, melt oil; add onion and garlic and cook over medium-low heat, stirring occasionally, until onion is tender. Stir in beans, thyme, and salt and pepper to taste. Cook until heated. Makes 4 servings.

Calories per serving: 42
Grams fat per serving: 2
Fibre: Good

BAKED LEEKS AU GRATIN

Though leeks are available nearly all year round, they're in season and most reasonably priced during the autumn. They're delicious with any cut of meat or poultry, or as part of an all-vegetable dinner.

4	large leeks	4
$\frac{1}{2}$ oz	butter	15 g
	Salt and freshly ground pepper	
4 tsp	grated Parmesan cheese	20 ml
1 tsp	water	5 ml

October-November Friday Night Dinner Menu
Lemon Chicken Schnitzel (page 90)
Baked Leeks au Gratin (pages 160–1)
Baked Pumpkin with Ginger (pages 164–5)
Tossed green salad
Deep-Dish Plum Pie (page 218)

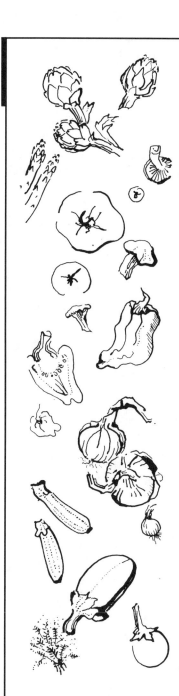

Trim base and tough green leaves from leeks, leaving tender green and white parts. Cut leeks in half lengthwise; wash under cold running water and drain. Place leeks, cut side up, in single layer in microwave dish or on lightly oiled foil. Dot with butter and season with salt and pepper to taste. Sprinkle cheese on top. Add 1 tsp/5 ml water to side of leeks. Cover dish or wrap in foil. Microwave on High for 5 to 7 minutes, or bake in 350°F/180°C/Gas Mark 4 oven for 25 minutes, or until tender. Makes 4 servings.

Calories per serving: 53
Grams fat per serving: 2.6
Fibre: Good
Vitamin C: Good

BRAISED RED PEPPER AND LEEKS

This dish goes well with lamb, pork or beef, but don't use more red pepper than called for—it could overpower the subtle taste of the leeks.

6	leeks	6
1	large sweet red pepper	1
4 fl oz	water or chicken stock	125 ml
½ oz	butter	15 g
	Salt and freshly ground pepper	

Cut dark green part and base from leeks and discard. Cut leeks in half lengthwise and wash thoroughly under cold running water. Cut leeks into ½ inch/1 cm thick slices. Remove core and seeds from red pepper; cut into thin 1 inch/2.5 cm long strips.

In saucepan, combine chicken stock and leeks; cover and simmer for 5 to 10 minutes or until leeks are almost tender. Add red pepper strips, cover and simmer for another 5 to 10 minutes, or until tender. If there is too much liquid, uncover and cook for 1 to 2 minutes. Add butter, and salt and pepper to taste. Makes 4 servings.

Calories per serving: 84
Grams fat per serving: 3
Fibre: Good
Vitamins A and C: Excellent

FOIL-STEAMED SPRING VEGETABLES

These vegetables are delicious with fish or chicken. In winter, use parsnips, mangetout or beans instead of asparagus and cut the carrots into $\frac{1}{2}$ inch/1 cm pieces. White pearl onions, which are the size of small grapes, keep for a month or two in a cool, dry place.

8 oz	fresh pearl onions	225 g
12 oz	fresh baby carrots	350 g
8 oz	asparagus	225 g
2 tbsp	water	30 ml
1 tbsp	butter	15 ml
1	bay leaf	1
$\frac{1}{2}$ tsp	salt	2 ml
Pinch	white pepper	Pinch

In large pot of boiling water, blanch pearl onions for 2 minutes; drain. Cut off root end and gently squeeze to remove skin. In another large pot of boiling water, blanch carrots for 2 minutes; drain, and rinse under cold running water; drain again. Snap tough ends from asparagus.

On large piece of foil, arrange vegetables in a single layer. Sprinkle with water, dot with butter and add bay leaf, salt and pepper. Fold foil over vegetables and seal. Bake in 375°F/190°C/Gas Mark 5 oven for 20–30 minutes or until vegetables are tender. Makes 6 servings.

Calories per serving: 65
Grams fat per serving: 3
Fibre: Good
Vitamin A: Excellent
Vitamin C: Good

Steam Cooking

To steam food means to cook over, not in, boiling water or other liquid. Foods wrapped in foil, then baked or barbecued, steam in their own liquids. Herbs, salt, sugar or spices can be added to the foods or to the liquid before steaming. The advantage of steaming is that vegetables retain their flavour, colour and vitamins; and fish is moist. Food can be steamed in the oven, on top of the stove or on the barbecue.

Equipment for steaming

There are a number of steamers on the market, but you don't have to have special equipment.
- Wrap foods in foil, then cook in the oven or on the barbecue.
- In top-of-stove cooking, you can use a deep pot with a tight-fitting lid and something to keep the food above the liquid. This could be a steamer with perforated petals and short legs, a flat-bottomed metal colander or one with feet, or a metal strainer. Large foods such as chicken or pudding can be placed on an inverted heat-proof plate or bowl, or a wire rack. A wok with a rack inside, and covered with a lid (or foil if the lid isn't tight fitting), can also be used.
- To oven-steam, use a roasting pan with a trivet, wire rack or anything that is heat-proof to keep the food above the liquid.
- Steam-cook in a deep-frier with basket set over water instead of oil.
- Use a clay baker.

SAUTÉED COURGETTES WITH YOGURT AND HERBS

Sautéed courgettes dressed with yogurt or sour cream is one of my favourite quick-vegetable recipes; because sour cream is higher in fat content, it is healthier to substitute yogurt.

1 lb	courgettes (about 3 small)	450 g
$\frac{1}{2}$ oz	butter	15 g
1	small onion, sliced and separated into rings	1
6 tbsp	plain yogurt or sour cream	90 ml
2 tbsp	chopped fresh parsley	30 ml
$\frac{1}{2}$ tsp	crumbled leaf oregano or 2 tsp/10 ml chopped fresh	2 ml
	Salt and freshly ground pepper	

Trim ends from courgettes. In food processor or by hand, slice them thinly.

In heavy frying pan, melt butter over medium heat; add onion and cook, stirring, until tender. Add courgettes and cook, stirring often, just until barely tender, about 5 minutes.

Remove from heat and stir in yogurt, parsley, oregano, and salt and pepper to taste. Stir to coat well and serve immediately. Makes 6 servings.

Calories per serving: 34
Grams fat per serving: 1.4
Vitamin C: Good

PARSNIP PURÉE

You can use carrots, turnips or pumpkin instead of parsnips in this recipe. When buying parsnips, remember the small ones are more tender and sweet than the older fat ones.

2 lb	parsnips	1 kg
½ oz	butter	15 g
4 tbsp	milk	60 ml
1 tbsp	sherry (optional)	15 ml
¼ tsp	freshly ground nutmeg	1 ml
	Salt and freshly ground pepper	

Peel parsnips and cut into chunks. Cook in boiling salted water until tender; drain and purée in a food processor, blender or food mill. Add butter, milk, sherry (if using), nutmeg, and salt and pepper to taste; process or stir until mixed. Return to saucepan to reheat or spoon into serving dish; cover and keep warm. (Purée can be prepared in advance and gently reheated before serving.) Makes 8 servings.

Calories per serving: 93
Grams fat per serving: 2
Fibre: Good
Vitamin C: Good

Puréed vegetables, because of their creamy texture, can be served instead of a vegetable with a cream sauce. Puréed parsnips team well with green beans, broccoli or other green vegetables that have been steamed or boiled. Serve with any meats or poultry. For a slightly milder flavour, combine puréed parsnips or turnips with mashed potatoes.

BAKED PUMPKIN WITH GINGER

Ginger goes particularly well with pumpkin. Grated orange rind also heightens the flavour and can be used instead of ginger. You could also use squash instead of pumpkin in this recipe.

2 lb	pumpkin	1 kg
1 oz	butter	25 g
2 tbsp	brown sugar	30 ml
1 tsp	ground ginger	5 ml
	Salt, freshly ground pepper and freshly grated nutmeg	

Cut pumpkin in half; scoop out seeds. Cover with foil and place on baking sheet. Bake in 400°F/200°C/Gas Mark 6 oven for 40 minutes or until tender. Alternatively, place in microwave dish, partially cover and cook in microwave on High for 7 to 10 minutes.

Drain pumpkin and scoop out pulp; mash or purée with 2 or 3 on-off or pulse turns in food processor. Stir in butter, brown sugar, ginger, and salt, pepper and nutmeg to taste. (Pumpkin can be prepared ahead to this point; transfer to baking dish and reheat, covered, in 350°F/180°C/Gas Mark 4 oven or microwave until hot.) Makes 6 servings.

Calories per serving: 93
Grams fat per serving: 4
Vitamin A: Excellent
Vitamin C: Good

BARLEY AND PARSLEY PILAF

Red onion adds crunch and tang to this intriguing rice dish.

5 oz	pearl barley	150 g
5 oz	brown rice	150 g
4 fl oz	hot chicken stock	125 ml
1	chopped red (or 6 spring onions)	1
2 oz	chopped fresh parsley	50 g
	Salt and freshly ground pepper	

Cook barley in 1¼ pts/750 ml boiling water for 30 minutes or until tender; drain.

In another saucepan, bring 16 fl oz/500 ml water to a boil; add rice, cover and simmer for 30 minutes or until rice is tender and water has been absorbed.

In 2½ pt/1.5 L casserole, combine rice, barley, chicken stock, onion, parsley, and salt and pepper to taste. (May be prepared in advance to this point.) Bake in 350°F/180°C/Gas Mark 4 oven for 20 minutes or until heated through. Makes 8 servings.

Calories per serving: 116
Grams fat per serving: 0.6
Fibre: Good
Vitamins A and C: Good

STIR-FRIED VEGETABLES WITH GINGER AND GARLIC

The wonderful combinations in this dish complement any meat from chicken and lamb to beef. You need only add rice to complete the main course. For a one-dish meal, add chicken, turkey, shellfish or ham to the stir-fry and serve over hot pasta.

4 oz	green beans	125 g
1	small courgette	1
2	carrots	2
$\frac{1}{2}$	small cauliflower	$\frac{1}{2}$
1	large broccoli stalk	1
1	sweet red or yellow pepper (or combination)	1
4 oz	mangetout	125 g
2 tbsp	vegetable oil	30 ml
1	red onion, thinly sliced	1
3	garlic cloves, chopped	3
2 tbsp	grated fresh ginger root	30 ml
2 tbsp	low-sodium soy sauce	30 ml
	Salt and freshly ground pepper	

Cut beans on the diagonal into $1\frac{1}{2}$ inch/4 cm lengths. Thinly slice courgette and carrots on the diagonal. Cut cauliflower and broccoli into florets. Slice broccoli stem crosswise on the diagonal. Seed peppers and cut into 1 inch/2.5 cm squares. Top and tail mangetout.

In large pot of boiling water, blanch beans, carrots, cauliflower and broccoli separately just until tender crisp. Drain, and immediately rinse under cold running water to prevent further cooking; drain thoroughly. (Vegetables can be prepared in advance to this point.)

Twenty minutes before serving, heat about 2 tsp/10 ml of the oil in heavy frying pan over medium heat. Add onion and 1 garlic clove; stir-fry for 3 to 4 minutes. Add courgette and some ginger and more garlic; stir-fry for 3 minutes longer, adding more oil if necessary. If pan is full, transfer vegetables to baking dish and keep warm in 250°F/130°C/Gas Mark $\frac{1}{2}$ oven. Add as many of the blanched vegetables as you can stir-fry at one time, plus some of the garlic and ginger, and cook, stirring, for 2 to 3 minutes or until hot; transfer to baking dish in oven to keep warm and continue stir-frying remaining vegetables, adding a small amount of water as necessary to prevent scorcing. Finish with peppers and mangetout, cooking until tender crisp. Combine all vegetables; toss with soy sauce, and salt and pepper to taste. Makes 8 servings.

Calories per serving: 67
Grams fat per serving: 3
Fibre: Good
Vitamins A and C: Excellent

ORANGE-SHERRIED SWEET POTATOES

These sweet potatoes can be prepared a day in advance, then reheated just before serving. They go well with turkey, goose or ham. Instead of sherry, you can substitute ginger, maple syrup or crushed pineapple (adjust amount to taste).

4	large sweet potatoes	4
$\frac{1}{2}$ oz	butter	15 g
	grated rind of $\frac{1}{2}$ orange	
4 tbsp	orange juice	60 ml
2 tbsp	(approx) sherry	30 ml
2 tbsp	brown sugar	30 ml
Pinch	freshly grated nutmeg	Pinch
	Salt and freshly ground pepper	

In pot of boiling water, cook unpeeled potatoes until tender, 30 to 40 minutes. Drain, let cool slightly, then peel. While still warm, mash potatoes with butter, orange rind, orange juice, sherry, sugar, nutmeg, and salt and pepper to taste. Return to saucepan and reheat over medium heat, or refrigerate until 1 hour before serving, then reheat, covered, in 350°F/180°C/Gas Mark 4 oven for about 25 minutes or until hot. Makes 5 servings.

Calories per serving: 208
Grams fat per serving: 3
Fibre: Good
Vitamins A and C: Excellent

MASHED SWEDE WITH CARROTS AND ORANGE

Adding mashed carrots to swedes, along with a pinch of brown sugar and a dollop of butter, mellows the swede and at the same time adds flavour to the carrots.

1	small swede	1
4	carrots	4
2 tbsp	brown sugar	30 ml
2 tbsp	orange juice	30 ml
½ tsp	grated orange rind (optional)	2ml
1 tbsp	butter	15 ml
Pinch	nutmeg	Pinch
	Salt and freshly ground pepper	
	Chopped parsley (optional)	

Peel swede and carrots. Cut into ¾ inch/2 cm chunks. Cook in separate pots of simmering water until very tender; drain. Mash each, either with potato masher or in food processor.

Combine swede, carrots, sugar, orange juice, butter, nutmeg, and salt and pepper to taste. Sprinkle with parsley (if using). Serve immediately or cover and reheat before serving. Makes 8 servings.

Calories per serving: 31
Grams fat per serving: 2
Vitamins A: Excellent

TURNIPS PAYSANNE

Many studies have associated frequent use of vegetables from the cabbage family or brassica family with reduced risk of cancer of the colon. The brassica vegetables include, swede, turnip, cabbage, broccoli, cauliflower and Brussels sprouts.

Either white turnips or a swede can be used in this recipe but the swede will take longer to cook. To save time use the food processor to slice the vegetables.

1	small swede or 4 white turnips (about 2 lb/1 kg)	1
2	celery sticks, sliced	2
2	large carrots, sliced	2
1	large garlic clove, chopped	1
1	onion, chopped	1
8 fl oz	chicken stock	250 ml
4 tbsp	chopped fresh parsley	60 ml
½ oz	butter	15 g
	Salt and freshly ground pepper	

Peel and dice turnips or swede (or slice in a food processor). In heavy saucepan, combine turnip or swede, celery, carrots, garlic, onion and stock. Bring to a boil; cover, and simmer until vegetables are tender, about 20 minutes.

Uncover and cook until liquid has reduced to a glaze. Sprinkle with parsley, butter, and salt and pepper to taste. Makes 6 servings.

Calories per serving: 54
Grams fat per serving: 2.4
Fibre: Good
Vitamins A and C: Excellent

MASHED POTATOES WITH ONIONS

These everyday vegetables are delicious when mixed. The onions add such flavour to the potatoes, you won't notice the absence of butter. Remember this recipe when you have baked potatoes. Scoop out the centre of the potatoes and mix with the rest of the ingredients. Spoon it back into the potato skins and reheat in 350°F/180°C/Gas Mark 4 oven for about 10 minutes. Or, if you are using another filling for the potato skins, use the scooped-out potatoes for this recipe.

6	potatoes	6
½ oz	butter	15 g
2	onions, finely chopped	2
1 tbsp	water	15 ml
4 fl oz	milk	125 ml
	Salt and pepper	

   Peel potatoes and cut into quarters. Cook potatoes in boiling water until tender, about 20 minutes.
   Meanwhile, in heavy frying pan, melt butter; add onions and water and cook over medium-low heat, stirring occasionally, until onions are tender, 10 to 15 minutes, reducing the heat if necessary so onions don't brown.
   Drain potatoes and return pan to stove; heat over low heat for 1 to 2 minutes, shaking pan to dry potatoes. Mash potatoes with half of the milk, adding remaining milk to taste (amount of milk needed will vary depending on size and kind of potatoes). Stir in onions, add salt and pepper to taste. Makes 6 servings.

Calories per serving: 123
Grams fat per serving: 2
Fibre: Good
Vitamin C: Excellent
Baked potato skins stuffed with Mashed Potatoes with Onions:
Fibre: Excellent for large potato

Compare
For maximum fibre, don't peel potatoes.

	Grams dietary fibre
1 large baked or boiled potato with skin	4
1 large potato, peeled then boiled	2

CURRIED FRUIT WITH RICE

New Year's Day or Easter Dinner
Sherry-Braised Ham with Curried Fruit with Rice (page 112)
Steamed broccoli
Green Salad with Parsley Dressing (page 85)
Poached Pears with Chocolate Sauce (page 190–1)

*To toast almonds, place on baking sheet and roast in 350°F/180°C/Gas Mark 4 oven for 5 minutes or until lightly golden in colour.

Light and juicy fruits plus curry make a fresh, pleasing combination. Along with rice, they go well with lamb or baked ham.

8 oz	cantaloupe or honeydew melon balls	225 g
6 oz	fresh pineapple, diced	175 g
1	banana, sliced	1
6 oz	sliced peaches, strawberries, grapes or mandarin oranges (or combination)	175 g
8 fl oz	chicken stock	250 ml
1½ tsp	cornflour	7 ml
2 tsp	curry powder	10 ml
4 fl oz	finely chopped chutney	125 ml
4 tbsp	raisins	60 ml
1 oz	butter	25 g
18 oz	hot cooked rice	500 g
4 tbsp	flaked roasted almonds*	60 ml

Combine fruits in bowl; set aside.

In saucepan, combine stock, cornflour and curry; mix well. Bring to a boil over medium heat, stirring constantly. (Sauce can be prepared ahead to this point; reheat before continuing with recipe.)

Just before serving, combine chutney, fruits (drained), and raisins; stir to mix. Add to hot curry sauce. Add butter; stir until melted.

To serve: transfer to serving bowl and sprinkle nuts on top. Place rice in a separate serving dish. Spoon some curried fruit over some of the rice on each person's plate. Or, spoon hot rice around edge of shallow serving dish; spoon curry mixture into centre. Makes 8 servings.

Calories per serving (including rice): 268
Grams fat per serving: 6
Fibre: Good
Iron, and vitamin C: Good
This curry sauce is mildly flavoured so as not to overpower the fruit.
Add more curry powder for a spicier dish.

BROWN RICE WITH CURRANTS

This healthy rice dish goes well with chicken, turkey, pork, lamb and fish.

3 oz	currants	75 g
2 tbsp	sherry	30 ml
½ oz	butter	15 g
1	onion, chopped	1
14 oz	brown rice	400 g
1½ pts	chicken broth	1 L
1 tsp	dried basil leaves	5 ml
	Salt and freshly ground pepper	

Soak currants in sherry and set aside until needed.

In heavy saucepan, melt butter over medium heat; stir in onion and cook, stirring, until tender. Add rice and stir to mix well.

Bring stock to a boil. Pour over rice; stir in basil, and salt and pepper to taste. Simmer, covered, until water has been absorbed, about 40 minutes. Stir in currants and sherry. Makes 8 servings.

Calories per serving: 112
Grams fat per serving: 2.5

CRACKED WHEAT AND BASIL PILAF

*If fresh basil is not available, use 8 tbsp/120 ml chopped fresh parsley and 1 tbsp/15 ml dried basil.

Keep this dish in mind for an all vegetable dinner or serve with meats or poultry.

5 oz	cracked wheat or bulgur	150 g
1 tbsp	oil	15 ml
1	large onion, finely chopped	1
2	garlic cloves, chopped	2
4 oz	thinly sliced mushrooms	125 g
1	large tomato, seeded and diced, or 1 tbsp/15 ml each tomato purée and water	1
8 tbsp	chopped fresh basil*	120 ml
4 tbsp	flaked almonds	60 ml
½ tsp	salt	2 ml
	Freshly ground pepper	

Rinse cracked wheat under cold running water; place in bowl and add water to cover by at least 2 inches/5 cm. Soak for 1 hour or until tender. Drain thoroughly.

In heavy frying pan, heat oil. Add onion and cook, stirring, over medium heat until tender. Stir in garlic and mushrooms and cook until mushrooms are tender, about 2 minutes.

Stir in tomato, cracked wheat, basil, almonds, salt, and pepper to taste; stir until mixed and heated through. Makes 6 servings (8 tbsp/120 ml each).

Calories per serving: 172
Grams fat per serving without almonds: 3
Grams fat per serving with almonds: 6
Fibre: Excellent
Phosphorus, vitamins A and C and niacin: Good

CAKES, BREADS AND BISCUITS

Nothing smells better than freshly baked breads and biscuits. And nothing tastes better either. Low in fat (if you don't spread on extra butter) and a good source of fibre and carbohydrates, the following scones and breads make excellent snacks and are an important part of every balanced meal. They also give you a chance to have sweet treats without all the fats, sugars and refined flours that lurk in most shop bought baked goods.

Moderation is the key to all good eating habits, and this applies to sweets as well. Enjoy them, but eat them in reasonable amounts.

| LEMON TEA LOAF

This lovely light, fresh tasting cake is perfect for afternoon tea but will equally make a wonderful dessert served with fresh fruit or sorbet.

7 oz	granulated sugar	200 g
2 oz	butter or margarine	50 g
1	egg	1
2 tbsp	low-fat yogurt	30 ml
4 fl oz	semi-skimmed milk	125 ml
9 oz	plain flour	250 g
1 tsp	baking powder Grated rind from 1 lemon	5 ml
Glaze		
	Juice of 1 lemon	
2 oz	granulated sugar	50 g

Line a 4×8 inch/1.5 L loaf tin with foil and grease lightly. In large bowl, cream sugar and butter or margarine. Beat in egg and yogurt then milk. Mix flour and baking powder; beat into egg mixture until blended. Stir in lemon rind.

Spoon into prepared pan; bake in 350°F/180°C/Gas Mark 4 oven for 1 hour or until skewer inserted in centre comes out dry. Let cake stand in pan for 3 minutes.

Glaze: In a small bowl, combine lemon juice and sugar mixing well; pour over top of the warm cake.

Remove foil and cake from tin and place on rack; loosen foil and cool completely before cutting. Makes 16 slices.

Calories per slice: 139
Grams fat per slice: 3
Grams protein per slice: 2
Grams carbohydrate per slice: 25

PUMPKIN MUFFINS

My daughter Susie has been making these muffins since she was seven years old. She makes them the night before we go on a car trip so we can have them for a very quick breakfast before leaving or in the car. Her only problem is keeping us from eating them that evening, so she hides them until the next morning.

3 oz	natural bran	75 g
4½ oz	wholewheat flour	135 g
3½ oz	granulated sugar	100 g
1½ tsp	cinnamon	7 ml
1 tsp	baking powder	5 ml
1 tsp	bicarbonate of soda	5 ml
½ tsp	salt	2 ml
5 oz	raisins	150 g
8 oz	mashed, cooked pumpkin	225 g
2	eggs (unbeaten)	2
4 tbsp	vegetable oil	60 ml
4 fl oz	plain yogurt or semi-skimmed milk and 1 tsp/5 ml vinegar	125 ml

In bowl, combine bran, flour, sugar, cinnamon, baking powder, bicarbonate of soda, salt and raisins; toss to mix. Add pumpkin, eggs, oil and yogurt; stir just until combined.

Spoon batter into paper lined or nonstick muffin tins. Bake in 400°F/200°C/Gas Mark 6 oven for 25 minutes or until firm to the touch. Makes 12 muffins.

Calories per muffin: 160
Grams fat per muffin: 5
Fibre: Good
Vitamin A: Good

Wholewheat flour contains 15.8 grams of fibre per 6 oz/175 g, while the same amount of plain contains 5.4 grams.

Wholewheat flour is made from the whole grain of wheat. Along with fibre, it also contains some fat. Plain flour has had the bran and germ removed from the wheat. It is enriched with the same nutrients naturally present in bran and germ, but it doesn't have the fibre or fat that wholewheat flour does.

Because of the fat content wholewheat flour doesn't have the same shelf life as plain flour, which will keep for up to two years. Wholewheat flour will keep 6 weeks to 6 months, depending on the milling method, before it turns rancid. For this reason, buy wholewheat flour in small amounts unless you use it regularly.

As a general rule, you can substitute wholewheat flour for half of the plain flour called for in a recipe. For example, if a recipe calls for 7 oz/200 g of plain flour, you can use 3½ oz/100 g plain flour and 3½ oz/100 g wholewheat flour.

Using all wholewheat flour results in a heavier product. In some cases, such as oatmeal biscuits, this is fine; in others such as cakes, it may be undesirable. Experiment with your favourite recipes to see how much wholewheat flour you can substitute.

This easy-to-make dessert, tastes wonderful, yet is low in fat and calories.

2 tbsp	plain flour	30 ml
3½ oz	granulated sugar	100 g
1½ tsp	baking powder	7 ml
3 oz	soft margarine	75 g
2	egg whites	2
1 tsp	vanilla	5 ml
5	small pears, peeled and thinly sliced	5

Topping

2 tbsp	plain flour	25 ml
1 pt	low-fat yogurt	500 ml
1	egg, lightly beaten	1
4 oz	granulated sugar	125 g
2 tsp	grated lemon rind	10 ml
1 tsp	almond extract	5 ml

In food processor or mixing bowl, combine flour, sugar, baking powder, margarine, egg whites and vanilla; mix well. Pres onto bottom of 10 inch/3 L square cake tin or loose-bottomed or flan tin; cover evenly with pear slices.

Topping: In bowl, sprinkle flour over yogurt. Add egg, sugar, lemon rind and almond; mix until smooth. Pour over pears.

Bake in 350°F/180°C/Gas Mark 4 oven for 70 minutes or until golden. Serve warm or cold.

Calories per serving: 235
Grams fat per serving: 6
Grams fibre per serving: 2

OATMEAL RAISIN MUFFINS

Serve these extra-moist muffins with fruit and yogurt or milk for a great quick breakfast. They are also delicious in a packed lunch.

4 oz	rolled oats	125 g
8 fl oz	semi-skimmed milk mixed with 2 tsp/10 ml vinegar	250 ml
6 oz	plain flour (or half wholewheat flour and half plain flour)	175 g
1 tsp	cinnamon	5 ml
1 tsp	baking powder	5 ml
½ tsp	bicarbonate of soda	2 ml
½ tsp	salt	2 ml
3 oz	raisins or chopped apricots	75 g
4 tbsp	vegetable oil	60 ml
3½ oz	brown sugar	100 g
1	egg, lightly beaten	1

Stir rolled oats into milk and let stand for 10 minutes.
Mix together flour, bran, cinnamon, baking powder, bicarbonate of soda, salt and raisins. Stir oil, sugar and egg into milk mixture; blend well. Stir dry ingredients into milk mixture, stirring just until combined.
Spoon batter into paper-lined or nonstick muffin tins. Bake in 375°/180°C/Gas Mark 5 oven for 20 to 25 minutes or until firm to the touch. Makes 12 muffins.

Calories per muffin: 124
Grams fat per muffin: 5

You can use this dough in our Deep-Dish Vegetable Pizza (page 139)

Food Processor Variation

In measuring cup, combine sugar and warm water; add yeast and let stand until bubbly. In food processor bowl combine wholewheat flour and 6 oz/175 g of plain, strong flour and salt. Add oil to yeast mixture. While processing, pour yeast mixture down feed tube. Process 30 seconds. Turn onto floured board and knead in enough remaining flour to prevent dough from sticking to board. Roll out as in Wholewheat Pizza Dough.

All-Dressed Pizza

Spread pizza dough with tomato sauce seasoned with oregano and basil. Then finish with your favourite toppings. Try
• chopped red, yellow or green peppers
• blanched broccoli florets
• sliced mushrooms
• sliced cherry or garden tomatoes
• artichoke halves
• grated mozzarella cheese
Bake in lower half of 450°F/230°C/Gas Mark 8 oven for 16 to 18 minutes or until crust is golden brown and cheese is bubbly.

WHOLE WHEAT PIZZA DOUGH

Use this basic dough for any type of pizza. Wholewheat flour adds flavour and fibre.

1 tsp	granulated sugar	5 ml
8 fl oz	warm water	250 ml
1	pkt active dry yeast or 1 tbsp/15 ml	1
8 oz	plain, strong flour	225 g
8 oz	wholewheat flour	225 g
1 tsp	salt	5 ml
2 tbsp	vegetable oil	30 ml

In large mixing bowl, dissolve sugar in warm water. Sprinkle yeast over water and let stand for 10 minutes or until foamy. Meanwhile, combine flours and salt.

Stir oil into foamy yeast mixture. Stir in about half the flour mixture. Add more flour, mixing until dough can be gathered into a slightly sticky ball (you may need a little more or less than 1 lb/450 g of flour).

On lightly floured surface, knead dough for about 5 minutes or until smooth and elastic, adding more flour as necessary to prevent dough from sticking to work surface. Cut dough in half; cover with greaseproof paper and let rest for 10 minutes.

On lightly floured surface, use a rolling pin to roll each piece of dough into a 12 inch/30 cm circle, about ¼ inch/5 mm thick.

Transfer rounds to 2 lightly oiled pizza pans or baking sheets. Carefully, using fingers, stretch dough into large circles.

Let dough rise for about 15 minutes before adding toppings. For a thicker crust, let dough rise for 30 minutes. Add toppings just before baking. Makes two 12 inch/30 cm pizza rounds.

Calories per Pizza: 855
Grams fat per Pizza: 16.5
Each Pizza will serve 4–6
Toppings add extra fat and calories

ALMOND MERINGUES

It's hard to find good-tasting biscuits that are low in fat. These are both.

4 tbsp	flaked almonds	60 ml
3	egg whites	3
3½ oz	granulated sugar	100 g
1 tbsp	cornflour	15 ml
½ tsp	almond extract	2 ml

Place almonds on baking sheet and toast in 325°/160°C/Gas Mark 3 oven for 3 minutes or until golden. Let cool. Reduce oven temperature to 225°F/110°C/Gas Mark ¼.

In large bowl, beat egg whites until soft peaks form. Continue beating, gradually adding sugar, then cornflour and almond extract; beat until mixture forms stiff peaks. Fold in almonds.

Line baking sheet with foil, shiny side down. Drop batter by small spoonfuls onto prepared pan. Bake in 225°F/110°C/Gas Mark ¼ oven for 1½ hours or until biscuits can be easily removed from foil. When cool, store in airtight container. Makes 30 biscuits.

Calories per biscuit: 22
Grams fat per biscuit: 0.5
A low-calorie biscuit.

OLD-FASHIONED MOLASSES BREAD

Moist and full of flavour, this bread keeps well. Serve for lunch with salad or soup or for afternoon tea.

6 oz	plain flour	175 g
6 oz	wholewheat flour	175 g
½ tsp	salt	2 ml
½ tsp	bicarbonate of soda	2 ml
2 tsp	baking powder	10 ml
3½ oz	skim milk powder	100 g
5 tbsp	wheat germ	75 ml
3½ oz	brown sugar	100 g
4 tbsp	chopped nuts	60 ml
3 oz	raisins	75 g
2 oz	finely chopped dried apricots	50 g
3	eggs	3
6 fl oz	orange juice	175 ml
4 fl oz	vegetable oil	125 ml
4 fl oz	molasses	125 ml
2	bananas	2

In a large bowl, combine flours, salt, bicarbonate of soda, baking powder, skim milk powder, wheat germ, brown sugar, nuts, raisins and apricots. In food processor with metal blade, in blender, or using electric mixer, whirl eggs until foamy. Add orange juice, oil, molasses and bananas; process until mixed.

Pour into dry ingredients and stir just until moistened. Pour into two 8×4 inch/1.5 L greased pans. Bake in 325°F/160°C/Gas Mark 3 oven for 1 hour or until firm. Let cool on wire rack, then remove from pan to cool completely. Makes 2 loaves (18 slices per loaf).

Calories per slice: 101
Grams fat per slice: 3.7
Two slices are a good source of fibre.

WHOLEWHEAT IRISH SODA BREAD

Variation
Raisin Wholewheat Soda Bread:
Add 5 oz/150 g raisins along with
flour.

After-Theatre Supper
Seafood Chowder (page 48)
Rocket and Radicchio Salad
with Balsamic Vinaigrette
(page 66)
Wholewheat Irish Soda Bread
(page 181)
Lemon Sorbet (page 197)
Coconut and Oatmeal Biscuits
(page 185)

Quick and easy to prepare, this bread dough can be mixed in
a few minutes, then popped into the oven. Serve with any
meal from breakfast to dinner.

1 lb	wholewheat flour	450 g
6 oz	plain flour	175 g
2 tbsp	granulated sugar	30 ml
2 tsp	baking powder	10 ml
1½ tsp	bicarbonate of soda	7 ml
1 tsp	salt	5 ml
1 oz	butter	25 g
14 fl oz	semi-skimmed milk, plus 2 tbsp/30 ml vinegar	425 ml

Combine flours, sugar, baking powder, bicarbonate of
soda and salt. Rub in or using a pastry blender, cut in butter
until crumbly. Add milk and stir to make a soft dough. Turn
out onto lightly floured work surface and knead about 10
times until smooth.

Place dough on greased baking sheet; flatten into circle
about 2½ inches/6 cm thick. Cut a large "+" about
¼ inch/5 mm deep on top. Bake in 350°F/180°C/Gas Mark 4
oven for 1 hour or until knife or skewer inserted in centre
comes out clean. Makes 1 loaf (about 16 slices).

Calories per slice: 143
Grams fat per slice: 1.7
Fibre: Good

WHOLEWHEAT RAISIN SCONES

Make these for a Sunday afternoon tea treat or to serve with salad or soup for a light supper.

2 oz	granulated sugar	50 g
6 oz	plain flour	175 g
6 oz	wholewheat flour	175 g
1 tbsp	baking powder	15 ml
1½ tsp	cinnamon	7 ml
½ tsp	nutmeg	2 ml
½ tsp	salt	2 ml
3 oz	butter or margarine	75 g
2	eggs, lightly beaten	2
5 tbsp	milk	75 ml
3 oz	raisins	75 g

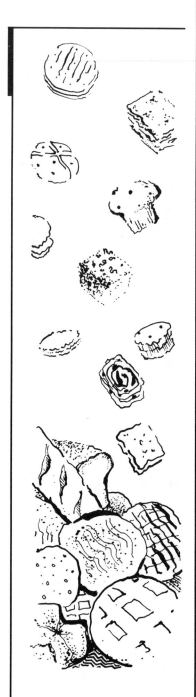

Reserve 1 tsp/5 ml of the sugar. In mixing bowl, combine remaining sugar, both flours, baking powder, cinnamon, nutmeg and salt. Rub in or using a pastry blender, cut in butter until mixture resembles coarse crumbs.

Reserve 1 tbsp/15 ml of the beaten eggs. Stir remaining eggs, milk and raisins into flour mixture and mix lightly. Turn out onto lightly floured work surface and knead about 5 times. Pat into a circle about ¾ inch/2 cm thick. Cut into 8 wedges and place slightly apart on greased baking sheet.

Brush reserved beaten egg over each wedge; sprinkle with reserved sugar. Bake in 425°F/220°C/Gas Mark 7 oven for 18 to 20 minutes or until browned. Serve warm. Makes 8 scones.

Calories per serving: 220
Grams fat per serving: 8
Fibre: Good

DATE SQUARES

Also sometimes known as matrimonial cake, these squares are very flavourful. If possible, use fresh pitted dates.

Date Filling

12 oz	chopped pitted dates	350 g
8 fl oz	cold black coffee	250 ml
2 tbsp	brown sugar	30 ml
	Grated rind and juice of ½ orange	
1 tbsp	lemon juice	15 ml

Crumb Mixture

8 oz	plain flour	225 g
1 tsp	baking powder	5 ml
½ tsp	bicarbonate of soda	2 ml
½ tsp	salt	2 ml
6 oz	butter	175 g
5 oz	rolled oats	150 g
5 oz	brown sugar	150 g

Date Filling: In small saucepan, combine dates, coffee, brown sugar and orange rind; bring to a boil. Reduce heat and simmer, uncovered, until mixture is soft enough to mash and has the consistency of jam (runny but easy to spread), about 10 minutes. Remove from heat; stir in orange and lemon juice. Let cool.

Crumb Mixture: Sift together flour, baking powder, bicarbonate of soda and salt. Rub in or using a pastry blender, cut in butter until mixture is the size of small peas. Stir in rolled oats and sugar. Press half of the crumb mixture firmly into 9-inch/2 L square baking pan. Spread date mixture evenly over crumb mixture and top with remaining crumbs, pressing lightly. Bake in 325°F/160°C/Gas Mark 3 oven for 25 minutes or until lightly browned. Makes about 25 squares.

Calories per square: 140
Grams fat per square: 5.6
Three squares are an excellent source of fibre.

ALMOND AND APRICOT SQUARES

Apricots add extra flavour to these tasty low-calorie squares.

4 oz	dried apricots	125 g
4 oz	butter	125 g
8 oz	wholewheat flour	225 g
4 oz	chopped almonds	125 g
5 oz	granulated sugar	150 g
4 tbsp	natural bran or wheat germ	60 ml
½ tsp	cinnamon	2 ml
2	eggs	2
½ tsp	almond extract	2 ml
½ tsp	baking powder	2 ml
½ tsp	salt	2 ml

In small saucepan, combine apricots with enough water to cover. Cover and bring to boil; reduce heat and simmer for 20 minutes. Drain, let cool and chop apricots finely; set aside.

In mixing bowl, cut butter into 6 oz/175 g flour. Mix in 4 tbsp/60 ml of the almonds, 4 tbsp/60 ml of the sugar, bran and cinnamon. Press half of this mixture into greased 8 inch/2 L square baking pan.

In another mixing bowl, beat remaining sugar with eggs and almond extract. Beat in baking powder, salt, apricots, remaining flour and remaining almonds. Pour over pressed layer in pan. Sprinkle with remaining flour-bran mixture. Bake in 350°F/180°C/Gas Mark 4 oven for 40 minutes. Let cool, then cut into squares. Makes about 18 squares.

Calories per square: 77
Grams fat per square: 4
Two squares are a good source of fibre.

Opposite:
Omelette à la Jardinière
(page 135)

RAISIN AND OATMEAL BISCUITS

These biscuits are a family favourite, especially of my son Jeff's, but don't eat too many.

6 oz	butter or margarine	175 g
5 oz	granulated sugar	150 g
3½ oz	brown sugar	100 g
1	egg	1
6 oz	wholewheat flour	175 g
4 oz	rolled oats	125 g
4 tbsp	wheat germ	60 ml
1 tsp	baking powder	5 ml
1 tsp	bicarbonate of soda	5 ml
8 oz	raisins	225 g

Cream butter, sugars and egg together thoroughly. Add flour, oats, wheat germ, baking powder and bicarbonate of soda; mix well. Stir in raisins. Drop by spoonfuls onto lightly greased baking sheets. Flatten slightly with floured fork. Bake in 350°F/180°C/Gas Mark 4 oven for 12 to 15 minutes or until light golden. Makes about 36 biscuits.

Calories per biscuit: 96
Grams fat per biscuit: 4
Three biscuits are an excellent source of fibre.

Opposite:
Pumpkin Muffins (page 175), Raisin and Oatmeal Biscuits (page 185), Breakfast Bran-and-Fruit Mix (pages 222–223)

WHEAT GERM CRISPY BISCUITS

Packed with whole grains, these low-fat, low-calorie biscuits are good for packed lunches, after-school snacks and desserts.

8 oz	wholewheat flour	225 g
2 oz	wheat germ	50 g
1 tsp	cinnamon	5 ml
¼ tsp	ground cloves	1 ml
¼ tsp	salt	1 ml
4 oz	butter or margarine	125 g
3½ oz	brown sugar	100 g
1	egg	1
1 tsp	vanilla	5 ml
2 tbsp	granulated sugar	30 ml

In bowl, combine flour, wheat germ, cinnamon, cloves and salt; mix well. In another large bowl, cream butter and brown sugar thoroughly; beat in egg and vanilla. Add mixed dry ingredients to creamed mixture and mix well.

Divide dough in half. On lightly floured work surface, roll each half ⅛ inch/2.5 mm thick. Cut with 2½ inch/6 cm round cutter. Place on ungreased baking sheets. Sprinkle with granulated sugar. Bake in 350°F/180°C/Gas Mark 4 oven for 8 to 10 minutes or until lightly browned. Let cool until firm, then remove from baking sheets. Makes 36 biscuits.

Calories per biscuit: 57
Grams fat per biscuit: 3

DATE MERINGUE SQUARES

One of my mother's recipes, these go well with frozen desserts such as Grapefruit Ice (page 196) or other fruit sorbets.

8 oz	chopped dates	225 g
6 fl oz	water	175 ml
3 oz	butter	75 g
2 oz	granulated sugar	50 g
2	eggs	2
1 tsp	vanilla	5 ml
4 oz	plain flour	125 g
4 oz	wholewheat flour	125 g
1 tsp	baking powder	5 ml
3½ oz	brown sugar	100 g
4 tbsp	flaked almonds (optional)	60 ml

In saucepan, simmer dates and water until mixture is thick and soft, about 4 minutes.

In mixing bowl, cream butter; beat in granulated sugar and mix well. Add egg yolks and vanilla; beat until well mixed. Beat in flours and baking powder until mixed. Pat into lightly greased 9 inch/2 L square baking pan. Spread date paste on top.

Beat egg whites until stiff peaks form. Continue beating, gradually adding brown sugar; beat until stiff. Spread over date mixture. Sprinkle with nuts (if using). Bake in 350°F/180°C/Gas Mark 4 oven for 35 to 40 minutes or until golden. Makes about 25 squares.

Calories per square: 125
Grams fat per square: 3.8
Fibre: Good

DESSERTS

Desserts are where we can really go astray when it comes to reducing the fat content in our diet. Most biscuits are deadly, and mousses, chocolate desserts and lovely whipped-cream confections are filled with fat. However, don't despair. This doesn't mean you have to deprive yourself forever of these delicious desserts. Just be aware of their high fat content and savour them in moderation. Save them for special occasions, enjoy small servings and select low-fat dishes for the rest of the meal.

This section of the cookbook has many delicious desserts that are not high in fat. Remember that fresh strawberries, juicy peaches and sweet cherries are among the delights of summer. And what tastes better after a two or three course dinner than a homemade fruit sorbet?

Many of the dessert recipes in this book are fruit desserts. They are low in fat, yet full of flavour. They are also high in vitamins, minerals and fibre. You will find them a delight to both the eye and the palate!

BLACKBERRIES WITH ORANGE CREAM SAUCE

In Vancouver, where I grew up, blackberries grow wild, and it wasn't until I moved to Toronto that I realized what a high-priced treat they were. One of my favourite events as a child was the annual family blackberry expedition. In just a few hours, we would fill large baskets with huge, juicy blackberries—lots to eat raw, some for pies and the rest to make into jelly.

| 1 lb | fresh blackberries | 450 g |
| 8 fl oz | Orange Cream Sauce (pages 220–1) | 250 ml |

Wash blackberries. Remove any stems. Spoon sauce into individual dessert plates and top with blackberries. Alternatively, spoon blackberries into stemmed glasses and pour sauce over them. Makes 4 servings.

Calories per serving: 126
Grams fat per serving: 0.7
Fibre: Excellent
Vitamin C: Excellent

STRAWBERRIES WITH RASPBERRY AND RHUBARB SAUCE

Compare: strawberries served with 4 tbsp/60 ml whipped cream instead of with Raspberry and Rhubarb Sauce.
Calories per serving: 146
Grams fat per serving: 10
Fibre: Good
Vitamin C: Excellent

Dress up strawberries, cherries, plums, blackberries or other fresh seasonal fruit with a delicious fruit sauce for a low-fat dessert.

1¼ lb	strawberries	600 g
12 fl oz	Raspberry and Rhubarb Sauce (page 220 ½ recipe)	375 ml

Wash, then hull strawberries. Serve them in stemmed glasses and pour Raspberry and Rhubarb Sauce over them. Makes 6 servings.

Calories per serving: 97
Grams fat per serving: 0.7
Fibre: Excellent
Vitamin C: Excellent

DESSERT TOPPINGS

Fruit pies with vanilla ice cream, whipped cream or worse, clotted cream—these innocent toppings can add disastrous amounts of fats and calories.

Ice cream varies considerably in the amount of fat it contains. Do read labels and choose ones with lower fat content.

Compare

Fat Content of Dessert Toppings	Grams fat per 4 tbsp/60 ml
Double Cream	24
Single Cream	10
Clotted Cream	32
Whipping cream (unwhipped)	20
Whipped cream	10
Imitation Cream	4–24
Sour cream (12% fat)	10
Whipped cream (pressurized)	16

	Grams fat per 4 oz/125 ml
Ice cream (vanilla, dairy)	12
Ice cream (vanilla, non dairy)	11
Yogurt (low fat)	1
1 oz/28 g Cheddar cheese has 8 grams fat.	

	Grams fat per 4 tbsp/60 ml
Custard Sauce (page 212)	2
Orange Cream Sauce (pages 220–1)	0.1
Raspberry or Strawberry Coulis (page 193)	0.1
Raspberry and Rhubarb Sauce (page 220)	trace
Easy Chocolate Sauce (page 221)	0.1
Sherry Orange Sauce (page 201)	trace

PEACHES WITH RASPBERRY YOGURT SAUCE

Peaches are a good source, and raspberries an excellent source of fibre.

You can use fresh or frozen raspberries or strawberries in this sauce. It's good over any fresh fruit.

4	fresh ripe peaches or nectarines	4
Raspberry Yogurt Sauce		
6 oz	frozen unsweetened raspberries	175 g
4 fl oz	plain yogurt	125 ml
1 tbsp	granulated sugar or honey	15 ml
Garnish		
	Fresh raspberries or mint	

Peel peaches (blanch in boiling water to make peeling easier) and slice.

Raspberry Yogurt Sauce: In food processor or blender, process raspberries, yogurt and sugar until smooth. Refrigerate until needed.

Spoon peaches into individual dishes and spoon sauce over peaches. Alternatively, spread sauce on plates and arrange peaches on top. Garnish with fresh raspberries or mint. Makes 4 servings.

Calories per serving: 141
Grams fat per serving: 0.3
Fibre: Excellent
Vitamins A and C: Excellent

POACHED PEARS WITH CHOCOLATE SAUCE

Poached fruit can be served in the poaching liquid. Remove cooled fruit from liquid and strain liquid. Boil poaching liquid until reduced to 8 fl oz/250 ml; let cool, then serve over poached fruit.

Many other fruits, such as peaches, plums, apricots and apples, can also be poached. Serve them with Easy Chocolate Sauce or one of the other fruit dessert sauces in this book, such as Raspberry Coulis (page 193).

1¼ pts	water	750 ml
3½ oz	granulated sugar	100 g
	Grated rind and juice of 1 lemon	
1	vanilla pod and/or cinnamon stick	1
4	pears	4
4 tbsp	Easy Chocolate Sauce (page 221)	60 ml

In large saucepan, combine water, sugar, lemon rind, lemon juice, vanilla pod and/or cinnamon stick. Bring to a boil, stirring until sugar is dissolved.

Peel, halve and core pears. Add pears to boiling syrup. (Pears should be covered in liquid; if not, double the amount of poaching liquid or poach in batches.) Reduce heat to medium-low and simmer gently for 15 to 20 minutes or until pears are almost tender (time will vary depending on ripeness and type of pear; remember, pears will continue to cook while cooling). Remove from heat and let cool in liquid.

Drain pears thoroughly and pat dry on paper towels. Arrange pear halves on individual plates. Drizzle with Chocolate Sauce. Serve at room temperature. Makes 4 large servings or 8 small.

Calories per small serving: 168
Grams fat per small serving: 0.8
Fibre: Good
Vitamin C: Good

RASPBERRY SORBET WITH STRAWBERRY COULIS

Don't strain the raspberry mixture; the seeds are an excellent source of fibre. Coulis is a purée of fruits or vegetables and is used as a sauce.

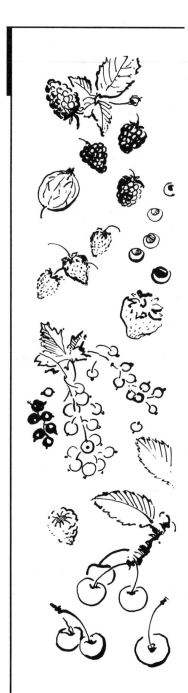

1 lb	frozen raspberries, thawed	450 g
8 fl oz	water	250 ml
1 tbsp	lemon juice	15 ml
8 fl oz	Strawberry Coulis (page 193)	250 ml

In food processor, purée raspberries. Stir in water and lemon juice.

Freezing Instructions:

Method 1—Ice-Cream Machine: Follow manufacturer's instructions.

Method 2—Food Processor: Freeze in metal pan or bowl until hard. Process in food processor until mixture is a hard slush. Return to freezer until needed.

Method 3—Hand Method: Freeze in metal pan or bowl until barely firm. Beat by hand or electric mixer until slushy. Return to freezer until needed.

To Serve: Sorbet should not be rock hard. If necessary, transfer to refrigerator 15 minutes before serving or process in food processor. To serve, spoon sorbet into individual dishes or stemmed glasses and pour sauce over it. Alternatively, spoon some sauce onto dessert plates and spoon a scoop or two of sorbet on top of each plate. (This looks very attractive when different kinds of sorbet are served on each plate and are garnished with fresh raspberries or other fresh fruits.) Makes 8 servings.

	Without coulis	With 4 tbsp/ 60 ml coulis
Calories per serving:	56	116
Grams fat per serving:	0.1	0.2
Fibre:	Excellent	Excellent
Vitamin C:	Good	Good

FRESH STRAWBERRY SORBET

Fresh, ripe strawberries make a delicious easy-to-make sorbet. Serve with other fruit ices or sorbets and fresh fruit, or with Orange Cream Sauce (pages 220–1)

8 fl oz	water	250 ml
7 oz	granulated sugar	200 g
1¼ lb	ripe strawberries, washed, and hulled	575 g
	Juice of 2 oranges	
	Juice of 1 lemon	
	Fresh strawberries for garnishing	

Bring water and sugar to a boil, stirring, to dissolve sugar; boil for 2 minutes and let cool. In food processor or blender, purée strawberries. Combine strawberries, syrup, orange juice and lemon juice; mix well.

Freeze and serve according to instructions in Raspberry Sorbet recipe (page 192). Garnish each serving with fresh strawberry. Makes 8 servings.

Calories per serving. 142
Grams fat per serving: 0.4
Vitamin C: Excellent

RASPBERRY OR STRAWBERRY COULIS

In blender or food processor, purée 8 oz/225 g frozen raspberries or strawberries. If using unsweetened berries, add icing sugar to taste. Makes about 8 fl oz/250 ml sauce.

Calories per 4 tbsp/60 ml: 60
Grams fat per 4 tbsp/60 ml: 0.1
Fibre: Excellent (when made with raspberries)

APPLE CINNAMON SORBET WITH RASPBERRY COULIS

A light, colourful year-round dessert. This sorbet is full of flavour and is very good by itself, or with Apple Sauce Wholewheat Cake (page 215), Pumpkin Muffins (page 175) or the Raspberry Coulis.

5 oz	finely grated, peeled and cored apple	150 g
2 tbsp	lemon juice	30 ml
2 tbsp	Calvados or apple brandy (optional)	30 ml
½ tsp	cinnamon	2 ml
1 pt	water	600 ml
7 oz	granulated sugar	200 g
1 pt	apple juice	600 ml
8 fl oz	Raspberry Coulis (page 193 full recipe)	250 ml

In frying pan, combine grated apple, lemon juice, Calvados (if using) and cinnamon; cook over medium heat, stirring, until apple is tender, about 3 minutes. In saucepan, bring water and sugar to a boil and cook until sugar is dissolved. Remove from heat; stir in apple mixture and apple juice.

Freeze and serve according to instructions in Raspberry Sorbet recipe (page 192). Serve it with fresh fruit such as grapes, sliced kiwi or strawberries, plus a fresh mint leaf, or drizzle with Raspberry Coulis. Makes 8 servings.

Calories per serving: 158
Grams fat per serving: 0.2
Fibre: Good
Vitamin C: Excellent

FROZEN LEMON CREAM

It's hard to tell the base of this creamy dessert is yogurt. It's also delicious with a topping of fresh fruit such as strawberries, peaches, bananas, papaya or kiwi.

1¼ pts	plain yogurt	750 ml
2 tsp	vanilla essence	10 ml
4 tsp	grated lemon rind	20 ml
4 tbsp	lemon juice	60 ml
3½ oz	granulated sugar	100 g

Combine all ingredients and mix well. Freeze and serve according to instructions in Raspberry Sorbet recipe (page 192). Makes 8 servings.

Calories per serving: 106
Grams fat per serving: 0.2
Calcium and phosphorus: Good

For a festive frozen dessert, use Frozen Lemon Cream as a filling between layers of Orange Sponge Cake (page 213) or sandwiched between Meringues (page 206), and freeze.

GRAPEFRUIT ICE

Fresh-squeezed grapefruit juice made into an ice is a delicious, refreshing dessert at any time of year. Arrange scoops of ice on individual plates with fresh grapefruit sections or other fresh fruit, or serve with biscuits or squares.

14 oz	granulated sugar	400 g
16 fl oz	water	500 ml
6	grapefruit (or 1½ pts/1 L carton of grapefruit juice)	6
4 tbsp	lemon juice	60 ml

In saucepan, combine sugar and water, stirring to dissolve sugar. Bring to a boil and boil for 5 minutes. Remove from heat. Grate zest from 1 grapefruit (take care to grate only yellow part—white part of rind is too bitter). Stir rind into syrup and let cool.

Squeeze juice from the 6 grapefruit to measure 1½ pts/1 L. Stir grapefuit juice and lemon juice into cool syrup.

Freeze and serve according to instructions in Raspberry Sorbet recipe (page 192). Makes 12 servings.

Calories per serving: 171
Grams fat per serving: trace
Vitamin C: Excellent

LEMON SORBET

A light, refreshing dessert. Compare the fat content of a serving of Lemon Sorbet with that of ice cream: 0.04 versus 8 grams.

	Grated rind and juice of 3 lemons	
16 fl oz	water	500 ml
7 oz	granulated sugar	200 g
1	egg white	1

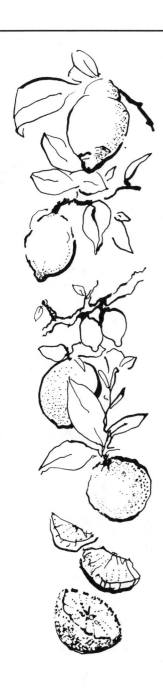

In saucepan, combine lemon rind, lemon juice, water and sugar; bring to a boil. Reduce heat and simmer for 5 minutes; let cool. Pour into metal pan and freeze until firm—at least 4 hours. Break frozen mixture into chunks, place in food processor and process until smooth. Add egg white and process for a few seconds longer. Spoon into freezer container; cover, and return to freezer until firm, about 1 to 2 hours. Place in refrigerator for 15 minutes, or until slightly softened, before serving. (To make without using a food processor, omit egg white and freeze according to instructions in Raspberry Sorbet recipe, page 192.)

Calories per serving: 152
Grams fat per serving: trace
Vitamin C: Excellent

YOGURT FRUIT FREEZE

This is a pleasure for dieters who are dessert lovers. It's also the perfect year-round treat for children.

1 pt	plain low-fat yogurt	600 ml
2	small bananas	2
5 tbsp	orange juice	75 ml
1 tsp	grated orange rind	5 ml

In food processor or blender, process yogurt, bananas and orange juice and rind until smooth. Alternatively, mash bananas and beat in remaining ingredients with electric mixer until smooth. Freeze and serve according to instructions in Raspberry Sorbet recipe (page 192). For children, freeze in lollipop moulds after processing. Makes 8 servings.

Calories per serving: 100
Grams fat per serving: 0.2
Vitamin C: Excellent
Calcium: Good

PRUNE CAKE

This easy-to-make cake is ideal for packed lunches or for feeding a crowd of children. Sprinkle it with icing sugar or ice with Lemon Icing (page 215)

8 oz	prunes, pitted	225 g
12 fl oz	water	375 ml
4 oz	brown sugar	125 g
2 oz	granulated sugar	50 g
8 fl oz	plain yogurt	250 ml
2	eggs	2
8 oz	plain flour	225 g
6 oz	wholewheat flour	175 g
2 tsp	baking powder	10 ml
½ tsp	bicarbonate of soda	2 ml
1 tsp	cinnamon	5 ml
½ tsp	salt	2 ml

In saucepan, combine prunes and water; bring to a boil and simmer for 1 minute. Cover and let stand until cool; drain.

In mixing bowl, combine sugars and yogurt; beat until smooth. Add eggs and beat until well mixed. Add flours, baking powder, bicarbonate of soda, cinnamon and salt; beat well. Stir in prunes.

Pour into lightly greased and floured 12 × 8 inch/3 L baking tin. Bake in 375°F/190°C/Gas Mark 5 oven for 30 minutes or until knife or skewer inserted in centre comes out clean.

When cool, ice with Lemon Icing (page 215) if desired. Makes 18 servings.

	With icing	Without icing
Calories per serving:	182	140
Grams fat per serving:	1.25	1.22
Fibre: Good		

MELON WITH RASPBERRIES

A quick-to-make, refreshing dessert. Or try it as a first course or breakfast treat. Peaches, grapes, kiwi or other fresh fruit in season can be used instead of raspberries. If serving as a first course, omit the honey; arrange wedges of melon on individual salad plates, drizzle with lemon juice mixed with liqueur or lime juice, and garnish with raspberries.

$\frac{1}{2}$	cantaloupe melon	$\frac{1}{2}$
$\frac{1}{2}$	honeydew melon	$\frac{1}{2}$
8 oz	watermelon cubes	225 g
6 oz	raspberries	175 g
2 tbsp	honey	30 ml
2 tbsp	lemon juice	30 ml
2 tbsp	melon or orange liqueur or sherry (optional)	30 ml
	Fresh mint leaves	

Cut cantaloupe and honeydew melon into cubes or balls. In glass serving bowl, combine cantaloupe, honeydew, watermelon and raspberries.

In small dish, combine honey and lemon juice; stir until mixed. Blend in liqueur (if using). Pour over melons; toss to mix. Cover and refrigerate until serving time.

Serve in stemmed glasses and garnish with mint. Serve at room temperature. Makes 6 servings.

Calories per serving: 122
Grams fat per serving: 0.9
Fibre: Excellent
Vitamins A and C: Excellent

CANTALOUPE, PEAR AND GRAPES WITH SHERRY AND ORANGE SAUCE

This sauce is easy to make and keeps well in the refrigerator for at least a week. Use any fresh fruit in season. Top this dessert with yogurt and brown sugar, or spoon over sorbet for another variation.

1	cantaloupe melon	1
1	pear, mango or papaya	1
6 oz	red, green, or black grapes	175 g
Sherry Orange Sauce		
$3\frac{1}{2}$ oz	granulated sugar	100 g
1 tbsp	cornflour	15 ml
1 tbsp	grated orange rind	15 ml
4 fl oz	orange juice	125 ml
4 fl oz	medium to dry sherry	125 ml
1 tbsp	lemon juice	15 ml

Cut cantaloupe in half; discard seeds. Cut flesh into cubes or balls. Cut unpeeled pear into cubes (if using mango or papaya, peel and cut flesh into cubes). Cut grapes in half if large, and remove any seeds. Spoon into stemmed glasses.

Sherry Orange Sauce: In small saucepan, blend sugar and cornflour; stir in orange rind, orange juice, sherry and lemon juice. Cook, stirring, over medium heat until sauce thickens, bubbles and becomes clear. Cook for 2 to 3 minutes, stirring constantly. Remove from heat and let cool.

At serving time, spoon sauce over fruit. Makes 6 servings.

Calories per serving: 166
Grams fat per serving: 0.4
Vitamins A and C: Excellent

LEMON CHARLOTTE WITH STRAWBERRIES

*Sponge fingers are often found in the biscuit section of supermarkets or shops.

Top this light, frothy dessert with your favourite kind of fresh fruit. Choose whatever is available—kiwi, raspberries, blackberries, or a combination.

7	eggs, separated	7
9 oz	granulated sugar	250 g
6 fl oz	lemon juice	175 ml
1	pkt unflavoured gelatine	1
4 fl oz	water	125 ml
28	(approx) sponge fingers*	28
12 oz	strawberries, blackberries raspberries or sliced peaches	350 g

In mixing bowl, beat together egg yolks and half the sugar until well mixed; beat in lemon juice. Transfer to top of non aluminium double boiler. Place over simmering water and cook, stirring, until mixture is thick enough to coat back of metal spoon, 8 to 10 minutes.

Meanwhile, sprinkle gelatine over water and let stand for 5 minutes to soften. Stir into hot yolk mixture; let cool, stirring occasionally.

Beat egg white until frothy; gradually beat in remaining sugar, beating until stiff peaks form. Stir one-third of the whites into yolk mixture to lighten, then fold into remaining whites.

Break sponge fingers in half. Line bottom, then sides, of 10 inch/25 cm springform pan with them, cut side in. Spoon in custard mixture. Refrigerate until firm, about 3 hours or overnight. (Cake can be frozen for up to 3 weeks; remove from freezer at least 1 hour before serving.)

Just before serving, place pan on serving platter and remove sides. Arrange fruit on top. Makes 10 servings.

Calories per serving: 326
Grams fat per serving: 6.6
Fibre: Good (Excellent if made with blackberries or raspberries)

LEMON CLOUD

This light, frothy lemon dessert looks like a mousse but
contains no cream. This one is easy to make but should be
served the day you make it; it can separate slightly if it stands
longer than a day.

2	lemons	2
$\frac{1}{2}$	orange	$\frac{1}{2}$
3 tbsp	cornflour	45 ml
$3\frac{1}{2}$ oz	granulated sugar	100 g
12 fl oz	hot water	375 ml
2	eggs, separated	2

Grate rind from 1 of the lemons and orange half.
Squeeze juice from orange and lemons (you should have
about 4 fl oz/125 ml lemon juice).
In non aluminium saucepan, combine cornflour and half
the sugar. Stir in water and bring to a boil, stirring constantly.
Reduce heat and boil gently for 3 minutes. Beat egg yolks
slightly; stir a little hot mixture into yolks; then slowly pour
yolk mixture back into saucepan. Cook, stirring, over
medium-low heat for 2 minutes. Remove from heat and stir in
juices and rinds. Transfer to mixing bowl and refrigerate to
cool slightly.
Beat egg whites until soft peaks form; continue beating,
slowly adding remaining sugar and beating until stiff peaks
form. Fold egg whites into lemon mixture. Spoon into
stemmed glasses or serving bowl. Refrigerate until serving
time. Makes 6 servings.

Calories per serving: 125
Grams fat per serving: 2
Vitamin C: Excellent

LEMON AND FRESH BLACKBERRY TART

Meringue on the bottom, lemon filling in the centre and blackberries on the top make a luscious, low-fat dessert that's lower in calories than a pie with traditional pastry.

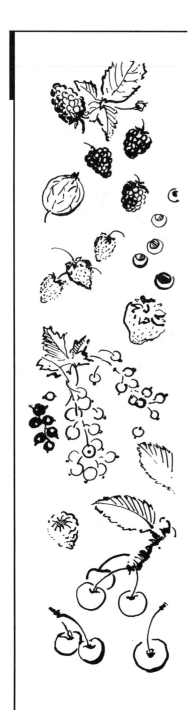

Meringue Crust		
2	egg whites	2
Pinch	cream of tartar	Pinch
3½ oz	granulated sugar	100 g
¼ tsp	cornflour	1 ml
½ tsp	vanilla essence	2 ml
Lemon Filling		
3½ oz	granulated sugar	100 g
5 tbsp	cornflour	75 ml
12 fl oz	hot water	375 ml
2	egg yolks	2
	Grated rind and juice of 1 large lemon	
	Grated rind of ½ orange	
Blackberry Topping		
4 tbsp	granulated sugar	60 ml
2 tsp	cornflour	10 ml
5 tbsp	water	75 ml
1 tsp	fresh lemon juice	5 ml
12 oz	fresh blackberries	350 g

Meringue Crust: Line an 8 or 9 inch/20 or 23 cm pie plate with foil; butter foil lightly, sprinkle with flour and shake off excess flour.

In medium bowl, beat egg whites with cream of tartar until soft peaks form. Beat in sugar, 1 tbsp/15 ml at a time, until stiff glossy peaks form. Beat in cornflour and vanilla essence. Spread mixture into foil-lined pie plate; bring sides about ½ inch/1 cm higher than pan. Bake in 300°F/150°C/Gas Mark 2 oven for 90 minutes or until firm and dry; let cool slightly on rack. While still warm, remove meringue from pie plate and peel off foil. Return meringue shell to pie plate.

Lemon Filling: Grate rind from lemon and ½ orange. Squeeze juice from lemon (you should have about 5 tbsp/75 ml). In non-aluminium heavy saucepan, mix sugar and cornflour. Stir in water and bring to a boil over medium heat, stirring constantly. Reduce heat and boil gently for 3 minutes, stirring constantly.

In small bowl, beat egg yolks lightly. Whisk a little hot mixture into egg yolks, then slowly pour yolk mixture back into saucepan, stirring constantly. Cook over medium-low heat, stirring constantly, for 2 minutes. Remove from heat. Stir in lemon juice and grated rinds. Let cool slightly; pour into prepared pie shell.

Blackberry Topping: In heavy saucepan, combine sugar and cornflour. Stir in water and lemon juice. Cook, stirring, over medium heat until mixture thickens, comes to a boil and becomes clear. Remove from heat and add blackberries, stirring to coat well. Spoon blackberries over lemon filling. Refrigerate for at least 30 minutes before serving. Makes 8 servings.

Calories per serving: 190
Grams fat per serving: 1.5
Fibre: Excellent
Vitamin C: Good

RASPBERRY MERINGUE TORTE

Make-Ahead Summer Dinner
Chilled Melon and Yogurt Soup
(page 37)
Cold chicken
Pasta Salad with Sweet Peppers
and Fresh Dill (pages 80–1)
Sliced tomatoes with basil
Wholewheat buns
Raspberry Meringue Torte
(page 206)

Frozen raspberries are available in most supermarkets, making this torte a year-round treat. It's not as complicated as it looks. The meringues can be made well in advance, and the custard sauce early in the day, or even a day in advance; neither procedure takes very long. Use strawberries or other berries when they are in season instead of raspberries.

Meringues		
6	egg whites	6
9 oz	granulated sugar	250 g
1 tsp	cornflour	5 ml
1 tsp	vanilla essence	5 ml
Custard Filling		
2 oz	granulated sugar	50 g
2 tbsp	cornflour	30 ml
Pinch	salt	Pinch
16 fl oz	milk	500 ml
4	egg yolks	4
2 tsp	vanilla essence	10 ml
Pinch	freshly grated nutmeg	Pinch
2 tbsp	orange or almond liqueur (optional)	30 ml
Fruit Layers		
1 lb approx	blackberries or sliced peaches, bananas, kiwi, mangoes or other fresh fruit	450 g approx
1 lb	raspberries or strawberries	450 g

Meringues: Line 2 baking sheets with foil; oil foil lightly. In large bowl, beat egg whites until soft peaks form. Combine sugar and cornflour. Continuing to beat egg whites, gradually add sugar mixture, beating until stiff peaks form. Stir in vanilla essence.

Spread meringue mixture over foil-lined baking sheet to form 2 circles about 11 inches/28 cm in diameter. Bake in 275°F/140°C/Gas Mark 1 oven for 2 hours or until meringues are firm. Remove from oven; while warm, carefully remove foil. (If foil is difficult to remove, meringues may not be cooked enough or foil wasn't oiled enough.)

Custard Filling: In non-aluminium saucepan or top of double boiler, combine sugar, cornflour and salt. Stir in milk. Cook, stirring, over medium-low heat or simmering water until mixture thickens and comes to a simmer; cook for 5 minutes, stirring constantly.

Beat egg yolks until mixed; gradually whisk a small amount of hot milk mixture into yolks. While stirring, pour warmed yolk mixture into hot milk mixture. Stir over low heat for about 2 minutes or until thickened slightly. Remove from heat; stir in vanilla, nutmeg and liqueur (if using); let cool.

A few hours before serving, place one meringue on serving platter; spread custard over meringue. Arrange blackberries or other selected fruit over custard. Place second meringue on top. Arrange raspberries or strawberries on top. To serve, cut into wedges. Makes 10 servings.

Calories per serving: 240
Grams fat per serving: 3.7
Fibre: Excellent
Vitamin C: Good

PEACH BLACKCURRANT CRISP

It's hard to find a better-tasting fruit dessert than this one. If you cook it in a microwave, it takes only 10 minutes.

2 lb	peeled, sliced fresh peaches	900 g
12 oz	blackcurrants	350 g
5 tbsp	brown sugar	75 ml
2 tbsp	plain flour	30 ml
2 tsp	cinnamon	10 ml
Topping		
4 oz	quick-cooking rolled oats	125 g
1 tsp	cinnamon	5 ml
4 tbsp	brown sugar	60 ml
3 tbsp	soft butter	45 ml

In 3 pt/2 L baking dish, combine peaches and blackcurrants. In small bowl, combine sugar, flour and cinnamon; add to fruit and toss to mix.

Topping: Combine rolled oats, sugar and cinnamon, rub in or using a pastry blender, cut in butter until crumbly. Sprinkle over top of fruit mixture. Bake in 350°F/180°C/Gas Mark 4 oven for 25 minutes or microwave on High for 10 minutes or until mixture is bubbling and fruit is barely tender. Serve warm or cold. Makes 8 servings.

Calories per serving: 255
Grams fat per serving: 5
Fibre: Excellent
Vitamin A: Excellent
Vitamin C: Good

PEAR CRISP WITH ROLLED OATS TOPPING

Adding powdered skim milk to crumb toppings is an easy way to add calcium and extra protein as well as flavour.

You'll enjoy the lemon and ginger flavours of the sauce in this autumn or winter dessert. The amount of juice will vary depending on the kind and size of pears used.

8	pears, cored and sliced	8
2 tbsp	lemon juice	30 ml
1 tsp	grated lemon rind	5 ml
1 tbsp	grated fresh ginger root or 1 tsp/5 ml ground ginger	15 ml
3½ oz	granulated sugar	100 g
4 tbsp	plain flour	60 ml
Topping		
3½ oz	brown sugar	100 g
5 tbsp	wholewheat flour	75 ml
3 oz	rolled oats	75 g
4 tbsp	powdered skim milk	60 ml
1 tsp	cinnamon	5 ml
1½ oz	butter	40 g

In mixing bowl, toss pears with lemon juice, lemon rind and ginger. Mix together sugar and flour; sprinkle over pears and toss to mix. Spoon into lightly buttered 3 pt/2 L soufflé or baking dish.

Topping: Mix together sugar, flour, oats, powdered milk, sugar and cinnamon; rub in or using a pastry blender, cut in butter until mixture resembles fine crumbs. Sprinkle over pear mixture.

Bake in 375°F/190°C/Gas Mark 5 oven for 30 to 45 minutes or until pears are tender and mixture is bubbling. Serve hot or warm. Makes 8 servings.

Calories per serving: 271
Grams fat per serving: 5
Fibre: Good
Vitamin C: Excellent

APRICOT CLAFOUTI

Apricots or other tinned fruit in natural juice can be used in this recipe, and others, just drain off juice and use.

Clafouti is a French baked-fruit custard dessert. It's easy to make and can be made with almost any kind of fruit besides apricots—cherries, plums, peaches, or whatever is available.

1 lb 12 oz	fresh apricots	800 g
½ oz	butter	15 g
6 tbsp	granulated sugar	90 ml
3	eggs	3
11 fl oz	milk	325 ml
4 oz	plain flour	125 g
1 tsp	grated lemon rind	5 ml
½ tsp	cinnamon	2 ml
2 tsp	vanilla essence	10 ml
Pinch	salt	Pinch
	Icing sugar	

Halve apricots, then pit them. Grease an 11 inch/27 cm glass pie plate or large quiche dish with the butter. Sprinkle with 1 tbsp/15 ml of the granulated sugar. Arrange apricots, cut side down, in dish and sprinkle with 2 tbsp/30 ml of the granulated sugar.

In blender or food processor, combine remaining sugar, eggs, milk, flour, lemon rind, cinnamon, vanilla essence and salt; process until smooth. Alternatively, beat remaining sugar with eggs; add remaining ingredients and beat until smooth. Pour mixture evenly over fruit.

Bake in 375°F/190°C/Gas Mark 5 oven for 50 to 60 minutes or until top is browned and filling is set. Just before serving, sift icing sugar over top. Serve warm or cold. Makes 6 to 8 servings.

	6 servings	8 servings
Calories per serving:	213	162
Grams fat per serving:	5.8	4.4
Fibre:	2.7 g	2.1 g
Vitamin A:	Excellent	Excellent
Vitamin C:	Good	Good
Niacin:	Good	Good

OLD-FASHIONED PEACH COBBLER

Make this old-fashioned comforting dessert in the summertime when peaches are juicy and plentiful.

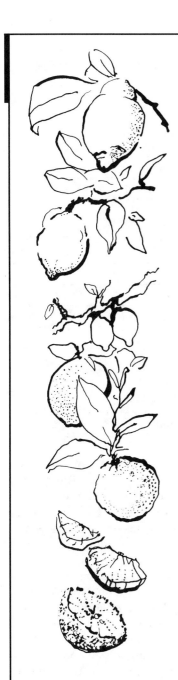

3½ oz	brown sugar	100 g
½ tsp	cinnamon	2 ml
1 tsp	grated lemon or orange rind	5 ml
1 tbsp	lemon juice	15 ml
1 lb 12 oz	sliced, peeled peaches	800 g
4 oz	plain flour	125 g
3½ oz	wholewheat flour	100 g
1 tbsp	baking powder	15 ml
4 tbsp	butter or margarine	60 ml
4 tbsp	granulated sugar	60 ml
1	egg, lightly beaten	1
4 fl oz	milk	125 ml
½ tsp	vanilla essence	2 ml

Lightly butter a 3 pt/2 L baking dish. In large bowl, combine brown sugar, cinnamon, grated lemon rind and lemon juice; mix well. Add peaches and toss in mixture; transfer to baking dish.

Combine flours and baking powder. In mixing bowl, cream butter and granulated sugar until light and fluffy; beat in egg. Add dry ingredients alternately with milk. Add vanilla essence, mixing just until combined. Drop batter by spoonfuls over peach mixture. Bake in 375°F/190°C/Gas Mark 5 oven for 25 to 35 minutes or until peaches are tender and top is golden brown. Serve warm. Makes 8 servings.

Calories per serving: 212
Grams fat per serving: 5.6
Fibre: Good
Vitamin A: Excellent
Niacin and vitamin C: Good

RHUBARB PUDDING WITH CUSTARD SAUCE

Tart rhubarb is a delicious contrast to this light sauce. The tartness will vary, depending on whether you use tinned, hothouse or home-grown rhubarb, so add more sugar if necessary.

2 lb	fresh or tinned rhubarb	1 kg
9 oz	(approx) granulated sugar	250 g
1 tsp	grated orange rind	5 ml
16 fl oz	water	500 ml
2 tbsp	cornflour	30 ml
4 tbsp	cold water	60 ml
1½ tsp	vanilla essence	7 ml
Custard Sauce		
2 tbsp	granulated sugar	30 ml
2 tsp	cornflour	10 ml
Pinch	salt	Pinch
8 fl oz	milk	250 ml
1	egg yolk	1
1 tsp	vanilla essence	5 ml
	Freshly grated nutmeg	

Cut fresh rhubarb into ¾ inch/2 cm pieces. In saucepan, combine rhubarb, sugar, orange rind and water. Bring to a boil; reduce heat and simmer, uncovered, until rhubarb is tender, about 10 minutes for fresh. Taste, and add more sugar if necessary. If using tinned rhubarb, just empty into a pan with juice and add orange rind with more liquid or sugar if necessary.

Mix cornflour with 4 tbsp/60 ml cold water; stir into rhubarb. Cook stirring, over medium heat until mixture thickens and becomes clear. Boil gently for about 3 minutes. Remove from heat and stir in vanilla essence. Transfer to serving bowl. Let cool, cover and refrigerate.

Custard Sauce: In heavy non-aluminium saucepan or top of double-boiler, combine sugar, cornflour and salt. Stir in milk. Stir over medium heat; bring to a simmer and cook for 5 minutes or until sauce is thickened slightly. Whisk egg yolk; whisk about 4 fl oz/125 ml of hot mixture into yolk. Whisk yolk mixture back into hot milk mixture. Cook, stirring, over low heat for about 2 minutes or until sauce is thickened. Remove from heat; stir in vanilla essence, and freshly grated nutmeg to taste. Cover, and refrigerate until needed. Makes about 8 fl oz/250 ml.

To serve, pour custard sauce over individual servings of rhubarb. Makes 8 servings.

Calories per serving
(including 2 tbsp/30 ml custard sauce): 183
Grams fat per serving
(including 2 tbsp/30 ml custard sauce): 1.4
Fibre: Good
Vitamin C: Good

ORANGE SPONGE CAKE

This cake is delicious on its own or with fresh fruit, dessert sauces or sherbets. Make sure you use large eggs at room temperature.

5 oz	granulated sugar	150 g
4	eggs, separated	4
1 tbsp	grated orange rind	15 ml
4 fl oz	fresh orange juice	125 ml
6 oz	plain flour	175 g
1 tsp	baking powder	5 ml
Pinch	salt	Pinch
2 tsp	icing sugar	10 ml

In mixing bowl, combine granulated sugar, egg yolks, orange rind and orange juice; beat until very light in colour. Add flour and baking powder; beat until combined.

In separate bowl, combine egg whites with a pinch of salt and beat until stiff peaks form. Mix a small amount of whites into yolk mixture, then fold yolk mixture into whites.

Pour mixture into ungreased 10 inch/1.5 L Angel Cake tin with removable bottom. Bake in 325°F/160°C/Gas Mark 3 oven for 50 to 55 minutes or until cake is golden brown and springs back when lightly touched. Invert and let cool completely before removing from pan.

Sift icing sugar over top, or ice with Orange Icing (page 215), or serve with sherbet or Raspberry Coulis (page 193). Makes 12 servings.

Calories per serving: 96
Grams fat per serving: 1.9

Angel food cake is very low in fat because it is made from egg whites only. However, you then have a lot of egg yolks to use up. For this reason, you may want to use a cake mix for making angel food cakes.

Serve wedges of sponge cake topped with Sherry Orange Sauce (page 201) and sections of fresh oranges.

CINNAMON YOGURT CAKE

Serve this easy-to-make, moist cake with fresh fruit or sorbet for any meal any time of day.

8 fl oz	plain yogurt	250 ml
1 tsp	bicarbonate of soda	5 ml
2 oz	butter or margarine	50 g
7 oz	brown sugar	200 g
1	egg	1
1 tsp	vanilla essence	5 ml
9 oz	plain flour	250 g
2 tsp	baking powder	10 ml
Topping		
3½ oz	brown sugar	100 g
1 tbsp	cinnamon	15 ml

Grease and flour a 9 inch/2 L square baking pan.
In small bowl, combine yogurt and bicarbonate of soda; mix well and set aside. (Yogurt mixture will increase in volume.)

In large mixing bowl, beat butter with sugar until well mixed. Add egg and vanilla essence; beat well, about 2 minutes. Sift together flour and baking powder; add to butter mixture alternately with yogurt mixture.

Topping: Combine sugar and cinnamon; mix well.

Spread half the batter in prepared pan. Sprinkle with half the topping. Cover with remaining batter and sprinkle with remaining topping. Bake in 350°F/180°C/Gas Mark 4 oven for 45 minutes or until knife or skewer inserted in centre comes out clean. Let cool for 10 to 15 minutes in pan, then invert onto wire rack. Makes 12 servings.

Calories per serving: 172
Grams fat per serving: 3.8

APPLE SAUCE WHOLEWHEAT CAKE

Full of flavour, this delicious moist cake looks attractive when made in an Angel Cake tin. It's easy to make and keeps well.

12 oz	granulated sugar	350 g
2 oz	butter, at room temperature	50 g
1	egg	1
4 fl oz	plain yogurt	125 ml
10 oz	apple sauce*	250 g
1 tsp	grated orange rind	5 ml
1 tsp	vanilla essence	5 ml
9 oz	plain flour	250 g
7 oz	wholewheat flour	200 g
3 tbsp	natural bran	45 ml
2 tsp	cinnamon	10 ml
2 tsp	bicarbonate of soda	10 ml
5 oz	raisins	150 g

Butter and flour a 10 inch/25 cm Angel Cake tin. In mixing bowl, combine sugar and butter; beat until mixed. Add egg and beat until light in colour. Add yogurt and beat until mixed. Beat in apple sauce, orange rind and vanilla essence.

In another bowl, combine flours, bran, cinnamon, bicarbonate of soda and raisins; stir to mix. Pour dry ingredients over apple sauce mixture and stir just until combined.

Pour into prepared pan and bake in 325°F/160°C/Gas Mark 3 oven for 70 to 80 minutes or until knife or skewer inserted in centre comes out clean. Remove from oven. Let cool on rack for 20 minutes, then remove from pan and place on wire rack to finish cooling. Makes 16 slices.

Calories per slice: 224
Grams fat per slice: 3.8
Fibre: Good
Vitamin C: Good

Serve cake with fresh fruit desserts, poached pears or sorbets.

Lemon Icing
Using yogurt instead of butter makes a creamy low-fat icing. In mixing bowl, combine 8 oz/225 g icing sugar (sifted), 2 tbsp/30 ml plain yogurt, 1 tsp/5 ml each grated lemon rind and lemon juice; mix until smooth.

Orange Icing
Substitute 1 tsp/5 ml each of grated orange rind and juice for lemon rind and juice.

*See recipe page 219, omit cinnamon.

RHUBARB CRUMB PIE

Welcome spring with this pie. A crumb topping reduces the amount of pastry needed.

Pastry

4 oz	plain flour	125 g
3 oz	wholewheat flour	75 g
½ tsp	salt	2 ml
2 oz	butter or margarine	50 g
3 tbsp	iced water	45 ml

Filling

7 oz	granulated sugar	200 g
4 tbsp	plain flour	60 ml
1 tsp	grated orange or lemon rind	5 ml
1	egg, well beaten	1
1 lb	sliced fresh rhubarb, cut into ½ inch/1 cm pieces	450 g

Topping

5 tbsp	brown sugar	75 ml
3 tbsp	quick-cooking rolled oats	45 ml
3 tbsp	powdered milk (optional)	45 ml
3 tbsp	wholewheat flour	45 ml
1 tsp	cinnamon	5 ml
1 oz	butter	25 g

Pastry: In mixing bowl, combine flours and salt. Rub in or using a pastry blender, cut in butter until mixture is crumbly. Sprinkle water over mixture and toss with a fork to mix. Press onto bottom and up sides of a 9 inch/23 cm pie plate.

Filling: Combine sugar, flour and grated orange rind; mix well. In another bowl, mix egg and rhubarb; add sugar mixture and stir to mix.

Topping: In bowl, combine sugar, rolled oats, powdered milk (if using), flour and cinnamon. Rub in butter until mixture is crumbly.

Spoon rhubarb filling into pie shell. Sprinkle topping over filling. Bake in 400°F/200°C/Gas Mark 6 oven for 50 to 60 minutes or until top is golden brown and rhubarb is tender. To prevent top from becoming too brown, cover lightly with foil after 30 minutes of baking. Makes 8 servings.

Variation
Rhubarb Crisp with Oatmeal Topping: Follow Rhubarb Crumb Pie but omit the pastry and reduce flour in filling to 2 tbsp/30 ml and omit egg. Combine filling ingredients and spoon into lightly greased 2½ pt/1.5 L baking dish. Prepare topping as above and sprinkle over rhubarb. Bake in 375°F/190°C/Gas Mark 5 oven for 40 to 50 minutes or until filling is bubbly and top is brown. Makes 6 servings.

Calories per serving: 234
Grams fat per serving: 3.6
Fibre: Good
Vitamin C: Good

Opposite:
Lemon Charlotte with Strawberries (page 202)

Calories per serving: 285
Grams fat per serving: 8
Fibre: Good
Calcium: Good

Should I Use Butter or Margarine?

Total fat consumption is the important risk factor in cancer: results from various studies don't identify one particular kind of fat, either saturated or unsaturated. However, since saturated fats and cholesterol may also be factors in coronary heart disease, it might be prudent to use a moderate amount of butter, solid vegetable shortening and lard; they are saturated fats high in cholesterol.

Saturated fats are mainly of animal origin, unsaturated fats of vegetable origin. However, it isn't that simple—some vegetable oils are hydrogenated to make them solid, and highly hydrogenated vegetable oils tend to raise blood cholesterol levels. When shopping, look for oils and margarines made from corn, sunflower, soybean, olive oil or safflower with as little hydrogenated oil as possible. When buying margarines choose the ones with the lowest amount of saturated fat.

The answer to what kind of fats to use in cooking is to use a variety but to keep the amounts as low as possible. Try cutting down the fat in your favourite recipes by a tablespoon/15 ml at a time to determine the minimum amount of fat necessary to produce a good-tasting result. I think you'll be surprised at how good many foods taste with less fat. By cutting out just one tablespoon/½ oz of butter, you reduce the fat content by 12 grams; cut out a tablespoon/15 ml of oil and avoid 15 grams of fat.

I like the taste of butter, so I use it wherever I will actually taste it, e.g. on steamed or boiled vegetables, or on toast when I'm not using jam (if using jam, omit butter or margarine—it's not necessary). This is a matter of personal taste and everyone should make his or her own choice as to what to "butter", as long as it is in moderation. I use margarine in baking or cooking where other ingredients overpower the taste of butter; for example, in gingersnaps I use margarine; in shortbread, butter; in muffins I use oil, because it is much quicker to incorporate. When frying or sautéing foods, use oil because it is lower in saturated fat. Be conscious of where you are using butter and margarine—often they aren't necessary. Peanut butter sandwiches don't need buttering, for instance, and butter is lost on hot-dog buns smothered with mustard and relish.

Opposite:
Peach Blackcurrant Crisp
(page 208)

DEEP-DISH PLUM PIE

Make this tasty fruit dessert in summer or autumn when plums are plentiful. The easy-to-make yogurt pastry is lower in fat and calories than a traditional pastry and is very easy to roll out.

Pastry		
3 tbsp	margarine or butter	45 ml
6 oz	plain flour	175 g
6 tbsp	plain yogurt	90 ml
Filling		
7 oz	granulated sugar	200 g
4 tbsp	instant tapioca	60 ml
1 tsp	cinnamon	5 ml
	Grated rind and juice of 1 lemon	
2½ lb	pitted and quartered fresh plums	1.2 kg

Pastry: In bowl, rub in or using a pastry blender, cut butter into flour until mixture is crumbly. Add yogurt and mix thoroughly. Form dough into ball, wrap in plastic and refrigerate for at least 1 hour. On lightly floured board, roll out dough into circle slightly larger than the size of baking dish.

Filling: In large bowl, combine sugar, tapioca, cinnamon and grated rind; mix well. Add lemon juice and plums; toss to mix. Transfer to lightly oiled 2½ pt/1.5 L soufflé or deep baking dish. Place dough over filling and press firmly against sides of dish. Cut slits in pastry to vent steam. Place on baking sheet and bake in 400°F/200°C/Gas Mark 6 oven for 50 to 60 minutes or until top is golden brown and filling is bubbly. If top browns too quickly, cover with foil. Makes 6 servings.

Calories per serving: 288
Grams fat per serving: 6
Fibre: Good
Vitamin C: Excellent
Vitamin A: Good

To reduce calories and fat content, make single-crust or deep-dish pies rather than double-crust pies. Or make a lattice top instead of a full top crust.

CINNAMON APPLE SAUCE

Serve this sauce with meats (especially pork) instead of gravy or other high-fat sauces, or as a dessert or breakfast fruit.

When making apple sauce, add the sugar after the apples are cooked. If you add the sugar at the beginning, the apples will take longer to cook.

Variation
Pear and Ginger Sauce: Substitute pears for apples and ginger for cinnamon in Cinnamon Apple Sauce; increase water to 8 fl oz/250 ml; add sugar to taste (Fibre: Good). Serve over Old-Fashioned Molasses Bread (page 180).

Apple sauce is so easy and quick to make, it isn't necessary to follow a recipe. Treat this one merely as a guide. The amount of sugar and cooking time will vary depending on the kind of apples and how ripe they are. To save time, don't peel or core apples; instead, pass cooked mixture through a food mill or sieve. If you want to keep the skin for more fibre and a chunky sauce, core the apples and chop coarsely; cook until apples are tender, then add sugar to taste. Grated lemon or orange rind or raisins can be added.

6	apples (about 3 lb/1.5 kg)	6
4 tbsp	water	60 ml
1 tbsp	lemon juice	15 ml
3 tbsp	granulated sugar	45 ml
1 tsp	cinnamon	5 ml

Cut apples into quarters. In saucepan, combine apples, water and lemon juice. Bring to a boil; reduce heat and simmer gently, uncovered, until apples are tender, about 20 minutes; stir often.

Place food mill or sieve over mixing bowl. Pass apple mixture through food mill or sieve (skin and seeds will stay in top of mill). Add sugar and cinnamon to purée; stir to dissolve sugar. Taste and add more if needed. Amount will vary depending on type of apple. (If sauce is too thin, return to saucepan and cook, stirring, over medium heat until it thickens.) Serve alone or with Apple Sauce Wholewheat Cake (page 215). Makes 6 servings.

Calories per serving: 101
Grams fat per serving: 0.5
Vitamin C: Good

RASPBERRY AND RHUBARB SAUCE

This sauce has a delightful sweet-tart taste that's perfect over ice cream, fresh or frozen yogurt and sliced peaches or other fresh fruit.

8 oz	sliced rhubarb, $\frac{1}{2}$ inch/1 cm slices	225 g
6 fl oz	water	175 ml
3$\frac{1}{2}$ oz	granulated sugar	100 g
	Grated rind and juice of 1 lemon	
$\frac{1}{4}$ tsp	cinnamon	1 ml
12 oz	fresh raspberries or frozen raspberries	350 g

In saucepan, combine rhubarb, water, sugar and lemon rind; bring to a boil over medium heat. Reduce heat and simmer until rhubarb is tender, 10 to 15 minutes. Remove from heat; stir in lemon juice, cinnamon and raspberries. Let cool. Serve warm or cool over vanilla ice cream. Makes about 1$\frac{1}{4}$ pt/750 ml sauce.

Calories per 4 fl oz/125 ml sauce: 110
Grams fat per 4 fl oz/125 ml sauce: 0.3
Fibre: Excellent
Vitamin C: Good

Compare
This is a creamy, low-fat dessert sauce; 1 tbsp/15 ml whipping cream has 5 grams of fat.

Variation
Orange Cream Dressing: Reduce sugar in Orange Cream Sauce to 2 tbsp/30 ml. Use with fruit salads.

Variation
Frozen Lemon Cream with Raspberry and Rhubarb Sauce: Spoon Frozen Lemon Cream (page 195) in layers into parfait glasses, alternating with Raspberry and Rhubarb Sauce (page 220), or pour the sauce over Frozen Lemon Cream. Use about 4 tbsp/60 ml sauce per person.

ORANGE CREAM SAUCE

Delicious over Lemon Sorbet (page 197) or with cake, this sauce also makes a creamy base for fresh fruit. For a nouvelle dessert, spread sauce over rimmed individual dessert plates and arrange three kinds of fresh fruit—strawberries, kiwi, sliced peaches, grapes or blackberries—artistically over the top.

4 tbsp	granulated sugar	60 ml
1 tbsp	orange juice	15 ml
	Grated rind of 1 orange	
6 fl oz	plain yogurt	175 ml

Cocoa powder is made from solid chocolate with the cocoa butter removed; therefore, it is much lower in fat than chocolate.

Choose chocolate recipes using cocoa powder instead of chocolate if other fat ingredients such as butter or oil, are in comparatively similar amounts.

Chocolate Milk
Combine 2 tbsp/30 ml Easy Chocolate Sauce with 6 fl oz/175 ml milk. Serve hot or cold.

*To measure golden syrup or honey on a spoon, dip metal spoon in hot water, allow to stand for a minute; you will then find the syrup pours off the spoon easily.

In small mixing bowl, combine sugar, orange juice and orange rind; stir to mix. Stir in yogurt and mix well. Makes 8 fl oz/250 ml sauce.

Calories per 1 tbsp/15 ml: 21
Grams fat per 1 tbsp/15 ml: trace

EASY CHOCOLATE SAUCE

Spoon this on ice cream, drizzle over bananas, pears or chocolate cake, or use as a dipping sauce for fresh fruit.

3½ oz	cocoa powder	100 g
5 oz	granulated sugar	150 g
6 fl oz	water	175 ml
8 tbsp	golden syrup*	120 ml
1 tsp	vanilla essence	5 ml

In saucepan, combine cocoa and sugar. Whisk in water and golden syrup. Bring to a full boil over medium heat; boil for 2 minutes, stirring constantly. Remove from heat and stir in vanilla essence. Let cool (sauce will thicken upon cooling). Cover and store in refrigerator. Makes 16 fl oz/500 ml sauce.

Calories per 1 tbsp/15 ml: 38
Grams fat per 1 tbsp/15 ml: 0.3

BREAKFASTS

The Breakfast Debate: To eat or not to eat

Food experts have long been telling us about the importance of starting the day with a good breakfast. In the '70s we were bombarded with the evils of a high-cholesterol, high-fat breakfast of sausages and eggs. Now some researchers claim the studies on the merits of eating breakfast are not conclusive and adults who don't want to eat breakfast shouldn't worry about it. Here are some reasons why we should eat breakfast.

Research has shown that the lack of morning fuel for children can affect their mental ability. Children who don't eat breakfast concentrate less than those who do. Children learn from example, so if you want them to eat breakfast, you should eat one yourself. Dieters often skip breakfast, yet studies show that it is easier to lose weight if you consume some of your daily calories in the morning. You will be more likely to burn these calories off, and you will be less likely to eat fattening, empty-calorie snacks between meals. The World Cancer Research Fund recommends weight control as one way to reduce cancer risk. It also wants us to eat more fibre-containing foods.

Breakfast provides an easy way to consume some of the body's needs for fibre, vitamins and minerals in the form of cereals and fruits; if you don't eat breakfast, it is harder to meet these requirements. On the other hand, those who do skip breakfast can pick up nutrients at a morning coffee break if they choose the right foods—fresh fruit, wholewheat rolls, wholewheat toast, yogurt, cottage cheese or low-fat cream cheese. Avoid energy-only calories and high-fat items such as Danish pastries, doughnuts, and too much butter. Because we need fibre from cereals as well as from fruits and vegetables, include both cereals and fruit for breakfast.

BREAKFAST BRAN-AND-FRUIT MIX

With this mixture on your kitchen shelf, breakfast can be ready in a jiffy—just add sliced apples, peaches, grapefruit sections, strawberries or banana, and top with yogurt or milk.

- Don't smother toast with butter.
- If using jam, omit butter altogether.
- Boil or poach eggs rather than frying them.
- Avoid bacon, Danish pastries and croissants.
- Don't limit yourself to traditional breakfast foods—left-over salads, rice, pasta or vegetable dishes, soups and sandwiches can taste just as delicious in the morning as at noon or dinnertime.

A Late Breakfast Menu
Honeydew, cantaloupe and watermelon wedges with Honey and Lime Dip (page 34)
Eggs Florentine with Yogurt Hollandaise (page 134)
Tomatoes Provençal (page 153)
Old-Fashioned Molasses Bread (page 180), or Wholewheat Raisin Scones (page 182)
Fresh berries and sliced peaches with Raspberry Coulis (page 193)

5 oz	bran flakes	150 g
3 oz	All-Bran	75 g
3 oz	sliced or chopped nuts (almonds, walnuts or pecans)	75 g
3 oz	chopped dried apricots	75 g
3 oz	chopped prunes	75 g
3 oz	raisins	75 g

Combine bran flakes, All-Bran, nuts, apricots, prunes and raisins; mix well. Store, covered in an airtight container. Serve with sliced fresh fruit and either milk or yogurt. Makes 10 servings.

Calories per serving
4 fl oz/125 ml semi-skimmed milk: 219
Grams fat per serving
4 fl oz/125 ml semi-skimmed milk: 7
Fibre: Excellent
Vitamin A and phosphorus: Excellent
Calcium, riboflavin, thiamin, niacin and iron: Good

BLENDER BREAKFAST

Keep this in mind for days when you want breakfast on the run; it takes only a minute to make and is packed with nutrients.

1	banana, peach or nectarine peeled and cut in chunks	1
4 fl oz	milk or plain yogurt	125 ml
1 tsp	honey, sugar or maple syrup	5 ml
1 tbsp	natural bran	15 ml

In blender or food processor, combine banana, milk, honey, bran; process until smooth. Pour into tall glass. Makes 1 serving.

Calories per serving: 217
Grams fat per serving: 3
Fibre: Excellent
Iron, phosphorus and niacin: Excellent
Calcium, vitamins A and C and riboflavin: Good

For other breakfast and light lunch dishes, see:
Eggs Florentine (page 134)
Omelette à la Jardinière
(page 135)
Baked Courgette Omelette
(page 144)
Broccoli Frittata (pages 132–3)
Cinnamon Yogurt Cake
(page 214)
Apple Sauce Wholewheat Cake
(page 215)

*See page 221 for method to measure honey

GRANOLA

This delicious, easy-to-make granola is one of the few granola recipes that doesn't use oil. Serve with yogurt and fresh fruit.

I lb	quick-cooking rolled oats	450 g
9 oz	wholewheat flour	250 g
4 oz	natural bran	125 g
4 tbsp	wheat germ	60 ml
1 oz	chopped walnuts or almonds	25 g
4 tbsp	sesame seeds	60 ml
4 tbsp	sunflower seeds	60 ml
½ tsp	salt	2 ml
8 fl oz	hot water	250 ml
8 tbsp	honey*	120 ml
1 tsp	vanilla essence	5 ml
5 oz	raisins	150 g

In large bowl, combine oats, flour, bran, wheat germ, nuts, sesame seeds, sunflower seeds and salt; mix well. In small bowl, mix together water, honey and vanilla essence; pour into dry ingredients and stir to mix. Spread on 2 lightly oiled baking sheets and squeeze mixture together to form small clumps. Bake in 325°F/160°C/Gas Mark 3 oven for 30 minutes or until golden brown, turning occasionally, so granola will brown evenly. Stir in raisins and bake for 5 minutes longer. Let cool completely. Store in airtight containers. Makes 16 servings.

Calories per serving: 250
Grams fat per serving: 5.3
Fibre: Excellent
Niacin and thiamin: Good
Calcium: Excellent, when eaten with 8 tbsp/120 ml milk.

WHOLEWHEAT PANCAKES WITH RASPBERRIES AND YOGURT

Use any fresh fruit in season as a topping. Peaches, strawberries and nectarines are delicious alternatives.

4 oz	wholewheat flour	125 g
3 oz	plain flour	75 g
1 tbsp	baking powder	15 ml
2 tbsp	granulated sugar	30 ml
½ tsp	salt	2 ml
1	egg, beaten	1
½ pt	skimmed milk	300 ml
2 tbsp	vegetable oil	30 ml
Topping		
4 fl oz	yogurt	125 ml
2 tbsp	maple syrup or honey	30 ml
12 oz	raspberries or other fruit	350 g

In mixing bowl, combine flours, baking powder, sugar and salt; stir to mix. Pour in egg, milk and oil; stir until dry ingredients are wet. (Don't worry about a few lumps.)

Heat nonstick frying pan over medium heat until hot (a drop of water will sizzle or dance.) Lightly grease pan if desired. Drop batter into frying pan from large spoon to form rounds. Cook until surface is full of bubbles that start to pop and underside is golden brown; turn and brown other side.

Topping: Combine yogurt and maple syrup or honey; mix well. Spoon yogurt mixture over each pancake and top with raspberries. Makes about 12, 4 inch/10 cm pancakes (2 pancakes per serving).

Calories per serving: 300
Grams fat per serving: 7.5
Fibre: Excellent
Calcium: Excellent
Riboflavin, niacin and iron: Good

*Available at health food shops.

SWISS FRUIT MUESLI

This Swiss breakfast is a complete meal in one dish. Keep a mixture of the dried ingredients on hand and add the wheat grains, fresh fruit and yogurt just before serving.

3 oz	wheat kernels*	75 g
2 oz	rolled oats	50 g
3 oz	raisins, chopped apricots or prunes	75 g
4 tbsp	chopped nuts (pecans, almonds, walnuts)	60 ml
	Fresh fruit (sliced peach, pear, strawberries, banana, apple or seedless red or green grapes)	
8 fl oz	plain yogurt	250 ml
	Honey or maple syrup (optional)	

In a bowl, combine wheat kernels, rolled oats, raisins or other chopped dried fruit, nuts, yogurt or milk; stir until mixed. Cover and refrigerate overnight. Top with fresh fruit before serving.

Calories per serving: 282 (will vary slightly depending on type of fruit used)
Grams fat per serving: 6
Fibre: Excellent
Calcium: Excellent
Niacin, riboflavin, thiamin, and iron: Good

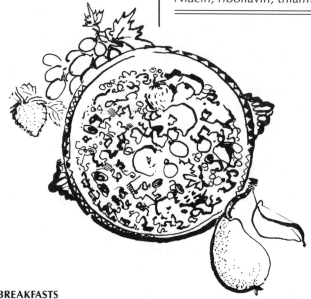

Breakfast Menus

Fresh fruit
Whole-grain cereal
Wholewheat toast
Yogurt or thin slice of cheese
Milk

Cantaloupe wedges
Bran flakes
Wholewheat toast
Yogurt

Fresh orange wedges
Wholewheat rolls
Poached egg
Milk
Coffee

Fresh fruit (melon, apple or
berries) topped with yogurt, and
sprinkled with cinnamon sugar
and wheat germ
Milk

Wholewheat pitta bread filled
with cottage cheese and raisins
Orange juice
Milk

Hot porridge with semi-skimmed
or skimmed milk
Half grapefruit
Wholewheat toast
Milk

Wholewheat toast spread with
low-fat cottage cheese and
topped with freshly grated
nutmeg and fresh raspberries or
other fruit
Milk

Swiss Fruit Muesli (page 226)
Yogurt and sliced peaches or
papaya

Quick Breakfast Menus

Orange juice
Granola (page 224) (made with
bran) topped with yogurt and
fresh strawberries
Milk

Honeydew melon with
strawberries
Wholewheat roll with melted
mozzarella cheese
Milk

Orange or apple juice
Breakfast Bran-and-Fruit Mix
(pages 222–3)
Milk

Wholewheat toast
Tomato juice
Blender Breakfast (page 223)
Milk

Weekend Breakfast Menus

Wholewheat Pancakes (with
Raspberries and Yogurt
(page 225)
Sliced mango with grapefruit
sections

Fresh fruit or stewed figs
Poached eggs on wholewheat
toast
Tomatoes Provençal
(page 153)
Coffee

Melon with Raspberries
(page 200)
Wholewheat Raisin Scones
(page 182) toasted and spread
with low-fat cream cheese

APPENDIX

To find out the ideal amount of fat you should consume in a day or how many grams of fat you need to cut per day:

1. First estimate how many calories you need in a day. Turn to page 229, refer to Table A (Estimated Average Requirements for Energy) and find your energy needs and corresponding calorie (kcal/day) requirement per day. Note: these are averages only.

> In the average British diet, 40 per cent of the calories come from fat. The World Cancer Research Fund guidelines recommend that no more than 30 per cent of your calories should come from fat.

2. Turn to Table B (Daily Total Fat Intake), page 230; find your closest calorie level. Then look across to the next column at the 30 per cent level; the corresponding grams of fat per day are the amount you can consume in order to have 30 per cent of your calories from fat. The difference in grams of fat between a 40 per cent level and a 30 per cent level is the amount you need to cut per day.

   For example, if you are a man consuming about 2500 calories per day with 40 per cent from fat, and you want to reduce to 30 per cent fat, your desired intake of fat would be 83 grams of fat, or a cut of 28 (111–83) grams.

   If you are a woman consuming about 2000 calories per day with 40 per cent from fat, and you want to reduce to 30 per cent fat, your desired intake would be 67 grams of fat or a cut of 22 (89–67) grams.

3. The following is another way to find out how many grams of fat you should eat in a day to have 30 per cent of calories from fat:

$$\frac{\text{Daily calorie requirement}}{9} \times .30 = \text{Daily fat intake}$$

Table A
Estimated Average Requirements for Energy

Children and adolescents

Age	Male	Female
0–3 mths	545	515
4–6 mths	690	645
7–9 mths	825	765
10–12 mths	920	865
1–3 yr	1230	1165
4–6 yr	1715	1545
7–10 yr	1970	1740
11–14 yr	2220	1845
15–18 yr	2755	2110

Adults

Age	Male	Female
19–49 yr	2550	1940
50–59 yr	2550	1900
60–64 yr	2380	1900
65–74 yr	2330	1900
75 + yr	2100	1810

From: Report on Health and Social Subjects 41. Dietary Reference Values for Food Energy and Nutrients for the United Kingdom, 1991.

Realistically assess the fat content in your diet. If you aren't overweight, rarely eat meat or rich desserts, use little butter, margarine, oils or mayonnaise and stay away from fried foods, you already probably consume 30 per cent or fewer calories from fat in your diet and don't need to reduce it any further.

The *Estimated Average Requirements* (EAR) for energy have been calculated based on energy intakes and expenditure. However, for individuals of 11 yrs and over the figures are derived from knowledge of their Basal Metabolic Rate (BMR), that is the amount of energy needed by a person in a rested state, ie, lying in bed. This figure is also dependant on their weight, heavier people therefore need more energy to maintain the same balance than do light people. The BMR is then multiplied by their Physical Activity Level (PAL), in this case 1.4 which is a figure assuming low activity levels at work and leisure to give EAR. However, individuals undertaking more strenuous activities in their work and leisure will have a higher PAL. This in turn will increase their energy needs—calories. For someone who is undertaking very vigorous daily activity, this could increase their energy requirements by half again. In any group of individuals there is a wide range of energy needs!

Table B
Daily Total Fat Intake According to Percentage of Total Calories

Calorie intake	% calories from fat	Grams fat/day
	25	33
1200	30	40
	40	53
	25	50
1800	30	60
	40	80
	25	61
2200	30	73
	40	98
	25	69
2500	30	83
	40	111
	25	83
3000	30	100
	40	133
	25	89
3200	30	107
	40	142

Table C
Fat and Calorie Content of Meat, Fish and Poultry

Type and/or cut	Portion 2 oz/56 g Grams fat	Calories	Portion 4 oz/112 g Grams fat	Calories
Beef				
Beef lean, average (raw)	3	69	5	138
Brisket, boiled 77% lean	13	183	27	365
Forerib, lean roast	7	126	14	252
Mince, stewed	8	128	17	256
Rump steak, lean only, fried	4	106	8	213
Rump steak, lean only, grilled	3	94	7	188
Silverside, lean only, boiled	3	97	6	194
Sirloin, lean, roast	5	108	10	215
Stewing steak, lean	6	125	12	250
Topside, lean only, roast	3	87	5	175

Type and/or cut	Portion 2 oz/56 g		Portion 4 oz/112 g	
	Grams fat	Calories	Grams fat	Calories
Lamb				
Lamb, lean, average (raw)	5	90	10	181
Breast, lean only, roast	9	141	19	282
Chops, (loin, lean only) grilled no bone	7	124	14	249
Chops, (loin, lean only) grilled, (weighed with bone + fat)	4	68	7	137
Cutlets, lean only, grilled	7	124	14	249
Cutlets, lean only, (weighed with fat + bone)	3	54	6	109
Leg, lean only, roast	5	107	9	214
Scrag and neck, lean only, stewed	9	141	18	283
Scrag and neck, lean + fat, stewed (weighed with fat + bone)	4	72	9	143
Shoulder, lean only, roast	6	110	13	220
Pork				
Pork, lean only, raw average	4	82	8	165
Belly rashers, lean + fat, grilled	19	223	39	446
Chops, loin lean only, grilled	6	127	12	253
Chops, loin, lean only, grilled (weighed with fat + bone)	4	75	7	149
Leg, lean only, roast	4	104	8	207
Veal				
Veal cutlet, coated in breadcrumbs, fried	5	120	9	241
Veal fillet raw, lean	2	111	3	122
Veal fillet, roast, lean	6	129	13	258
Chicken				
Boiled, meat only, light and dark	4	102	8	205
light meat, boiled	3	91	5	183
dark meat, boiled	6	114	11	228
roast meat only, light and dark	3	83	6	166
roast, meat and skin	8	121	16	242
roast, light meat	2	80	5	159
roast, dark meat	4	87	8	174
wing quarter roast, meat only, (weighed with bone)	2	41	3	83
leg quarter, roast, meat only (weighed with bone)	2	51	4	103
breaded and fried	8	136	17	271
Duck, roast, meat only	5	106	11	212
Goose, roast, meat only	13	178	25	357
Grouse, roast, meat only	3	97	6	194
Partridge, roast, meat only	4	119	8	237
Pheasant, roast, meat only	5	119	10	239
Pigeon, roast, meat only	7	129	15	258

Type and/or cut	Portion 2 oz/56 g		Portion 4 oz/112 g	
	Grams fat	Calories	Grams fat	Calories
Turkey, roast meat, light and dark	2	78	3	157
Turkey, roast, light meat	1	74	2	148
Turkey, roast, dark meat	2	83	5	166
Hare, stewed meat only	5	108	9	215
Rabbit, stewed, meat only	4	100	9	200
Venison, roast	6	111	7	222
Heart, Ox, stewed	3	100	7	200
Kidney, lamb, fried	3	89	7	174
Kidney, pig, stewed	3	86	7	171
Liver, lamb, fried	8	130	16	260
Liver, ox, stewed	5	111	11	222
Liver, pig, stewed	5	106	9	212
Tongue, Ox, boiled	13	164	27	328
Meat Products				
Beefburger, fried	10	148	19	296
Black Pudding, fried	12	171	25	342
Corned Beef	7	122	14	243
Grillsteaks, beef, grilled	13	171	27	341
chopped Ham and Pork, canned	13	154	26	308
Liver Sausage	15	174	30	347
Luncheon Meat, canned	15	175	30	350
Paté, liver	16	177	32	354
Paté, low fat	7	107	13	214
Salami	25	225	50	550
Sausages, pork, grilled	14	178	28	356
Sausages, low fat, grilled	6	128	15	256
Fish				
Cod, poached, no bones	0.6	54	1	108
Cod in batter, fried	6	111	12	222
Haddock, steamed, no bones	0.5	55	1	110
Haddock, crumbled and fried, no bones	5	97	9	195
Halibut, steamed, no bones	2	73	5	147
Lemon Sole, steamed	0.5	52	1	101
Plaice, fillets, crumbed and fried	8	128	15	255
Whiting, steamed, no bones	0.5	52	1	103
Herring, grilled, no bones	7	111	15	223
Mackerel, fried, no bones	5	77	9	155
Pilchards in tomato sauce	3	71	6	141
Salmon, canned, no bones	5	87	9	174
Salmon, smoked	3	86	5	160
Sardines in tomato sauce	6	99	13	198
Tuna in brine	0.3	55	0.7	111
Crab, boiled	3	71	6	142

Type and/or cut	Portion 2 oz/56 g		Portion 4 oz/112 g	
	Grams fat	Calories	Grams fat	Calories
Prawns, boiled, no shell	1	60	2	120
Scampi, crumbed and fried	10	177	20	353
Shrimps, canned	0.7	53	1.3	105
Mussels, boiled with shell	0.3	15	0.7	29
Fish fingers, grilled	5	120	11	239
Cod Roe, hard, fried	6	113	13	226
Taramasalata	26	250	52	500

Source: McCance and Widdowson's, The Composition of Foods, Fifth Edition, 1991.
Note: Discrepancies in figures due to rounding up or down.
Meat loses about 25% weight on average when cooked.

Table D
Fat and Calorie Content of Cheese

Type	Grams fat/1 oz/28 g	Calories/1oz/28g
Cheese spread	6.5	78
Full Fat Soft Cheese	8.7	89
Danish Blue	8.4	98
Brie	7.6	90
Camembert	6.7	84.0
Cheddar	9.8	117
Cheddar type, reduced fat	4.3	74
Processed slices	7.7	94
Medium fat soft cheese	4.1	51
Cottage cheese, plain	1.1	28
Cottage cheese, reduced fat	0.4	22
Cottage cheese, with additions	1.1	27
Cream cheese	13.4	124
Edam cheese	7.2	94
Feta cheese	5.7	71
Gouda	8.8	106
Gruyére	9.4	116
Mozzarella	6.0	82
Parmesan, grated	7.65	94
Ricotta	3.1	41
Roquefort	9.3	106
Swiss Emmental	8.4	108
Fromage frais, plain	2.0	32
Fromage frais, very low fat	Trace	16
Fromage frais, fruit	1.6	37

28 g = 1 oz = 50 ml of grated or chopped or crumbled Cheddar or other hard cheese
= 25 ml of cottage or cream cheese
The fourth supplement to McCance and Widdowson's, The Composition of Foods (4th Edition) 1989

Table E
Fat Content of Dairy Products, Fats and Oils

	Grams fat/ 1 tbsp/15 ml
Butter	12.3
Low fat spread	6.1
Very low fat spread	3.4
Margarine	12.2
Coffee Compliment/Coffeemate	5.3
Half cream	2.0
Double cream	7.2
Soured cream	2.9
Yogurt (low fat)	0.1
Yogurt (whole milk)	0.5
Oils (corn, safflower, olive)	15

Salad Dressings

French Dressing	11.0
Blue/Roquefort	8.1
Mayonnaise	11.3
Mayonnaise, reduced calorie	4.2
Reduced french mayonnaise	4.0
Thousand Island	5.0

	Grams fat per 4 fl oz/125 ml
Milk, Ice Cream, Frozen Desserts	
Whole milk	4.9
Semi-skimmed milk	2
Skim milk	0.1
Ice Cream	14
Sorbet	0
Channel Island milk	6.4
Goats milk	4.4
Soya milk	2.4
Milk shakes	(as per milk used in shake)
Choc Ices	6.5 per choc ice
Ice lolly	0 per lolly

Source: The fourth supplement to McCance and Widdowson's, The Composition of Foods (4th edition) 1989 and manufacturer's own data 1990

Table F
Breakfast Cereal by Fibre Content

Excellent Source of fibre

(over 4 g of fibre per 1oz/28 g serving)

Cereal Name	Fibre/1 oz = serving
All Bran	6.9
Bran Buds	5.7
Farmhouse Bran	5.1*
Sultana Bran	2.8

Good Source of Fibre

(2 to 3.9 g of fibre per 1 oz/28 g serving)

Bran Flakes	3.2
Fruit 'n Fibre	2.0
Muesli with no added sugar	2.2
Nutri-Grain	2.5
Ready Brek	2.0
Shredded Wheat (1 biscuit)	2.8
Shreddies	2.7
Weetabix (1 biscuit = 18.7 g)	2.7
Weetaflake	2.7
Weetaflake 'n raisin	2.0*
Weetos	3.3*

Under 2 g of fibre per 1 oz/28 g serving

Coco Pops	0.2
Cornflakes	0.3
Crunchy Nut Cornflakes	0.2
Frosties	0.1
Grapenuts	1.8*
Honey Smacks	1.3
Muesli, Swiss Style	1.7
Muesli, with extra fruit	1.5*
Porridge—made with milk or water	0.2
Puffed Wheat	1.5
Rice Crispies	0.1
Ricicles	0.1
Special K	0.6
Start	1.3
Sugar Puffs	0.9

Source: The third supplement to McCance and Widdowson's, The Composition of Foods (4th edition) 1988.
All figures for fibre measured by Englyst method, except those* which are measured by Southgate method.
Special note: All these figures are based on serving sizes of 1 oz = 28 g, however, some cereals eg. All Bran, Weetabix, Shredded Wheat may have serving sizes sometimes larger, the fibre figure will therefore be larger.
Porridge will be a serving about 6–8 oz, so immediately the figure is higher.

Table G
Vegetable Fibre Values

Vegetable	Serving size†	Grams dietary fibre/serving	Dietary fibre/100 grams
Beans, red kidney	3½ oz/100 g	6.7	6.7
Baked beans	5 oz/150 g	5.3	3.5
Beetroot, red, cooked	2	1.9	1.9
Broccoli, fresh or frozen, cooked	3½ oz/100 g	2.3	2.3
Brussels sprouts, cooked	4	1.5	2.3
Cabbage, red or green, raw, chopped	1 oz/28 g	0.7	2.4
Carrots, sliced cooked	3½ oz/100 g	2.5	2.5
raw	1	1.5	2.5
Cauliflower, raw, chopped	2 oz/56 g	0.9	1.8
Celery, raw,	3	0.5	1.1
Courgette	1	0.5	0.5
Cucumber (not peeled)	1 oz/28 g	0.2	0.6
Lentils, cooked	3½ oz/100 g	1.9	1.9
Lettuce (iceberg)	2–3 leaves	0.1	0.6
Mushrooms, raw	2 oz/56 g	0.7	1.1
Parsnips, cooked, mashed	3½ oz/100 g	4.7	4.7
Peas, green frozen, cooked	3½ oz/100 g	4.5	4.5
Pepper, sweet, red or green, raw	1 medium	1.6	1.6
cooked	1 medium	1.8	1.8
Potatoes, boiled in skin	1 medium	2.7	1.5
peeled, boiled	1 medium	2.0	1.1
Spinach, fresh, frozen or canned, cooked, drained	3½ oz/100 g	2.1	2.1
Sweetcorn	3½ oz/100 g	2.0	2.0
Swede, boiled	3½ oz/100 g	0.7	0.7
Sweet potato, boiled in skin	1 large	4.6	2.3
Tomato, ripe, raw, unpeeled	1 medium	0.7	1.0
Turnip, boiled, mashed	3½ oz/100 g	1.9	1.9

Source: The fifth supplement to McCance and Widdowson's, The Composition of Foods (4th edition) 1991.

All figures measured by the Englyst method.

Dishes Containing an Excellent Source of Vitamin C

(More than 15 mg per serving)

Soup Dishes
Chicken and Leek Chowder
Chilled Yogurt and Melon Soup
Corn and Tomato Chowder with Tarragon
Cream of Broccoli Soup
Fish Chowder, Family Style
Fresh Tomato and Basil Soup
Gazpacho
Potage Vert
Vegetable Soup
Summer Garden Italian Soup with Pesto
Tomato and Bean Chowder

Salads
Artichoke and Tomato Salad
Rocket and Radicchio Salad with Balsamic
    Vinaigrette
Bermuda Bean Salad
Broccoli Buffet Salad
Chicken and Melon Salad
Chick Pea Salad with Red Onion and
    Tomato
Coleslaw with Apple and Onion
Cracked Wheat with Peas and Onions
Greek Salad
Julienne Vegetable Salad with Lemon
    Vinaigrette
Melon and Bean Salad
Pasta Salad with Sweet Peppers and Dill
Red Potato Salad with Sour Cream and
    Chives
Spinach and Red Cabbage Salad with Blue
    Cheese Dressing
Spinach Supper Salad
Tabbouleh
Tomato Raita
White Kidney Bean Salad

Vegetables
Asparagus with Red Pepper Purée
Braised Red Cabbage
Braised Red Peppers and Leeks
Broccoli Frittata
Broccoli and Sweet Pepper Stir-Fry
Glazed Brussels Sprouts with Pecans
Mashed Potatoes with Onions
Orange Sherried Sweet Potatoes
Scalloped Cabbage au Gratin
Stir-Fried Vegetables with Ginger and Garlic
Tomato Raita
Tomatoes Florentine
Tomatoes Provençal
Two-Cabbage Stir-Fry
Turnips Paysanne

Dishes Containing an Excellent Source of Vitamin A

(More than 1,200 I.U. per serving)

Soups
Chicken and Leek Chowder
Chilled Melon and Yogurt Soup
Cream of Broccoli Soup
Fish Chowder, Family Style
Fresh Tomato and Basil Soup
Seafood Chowder
Red Lentil Soup
Vegetable Soup
Summer Garden Italian Soup with Pesto

Salads and Vegetables
Asparagus with Red Pepper Purée
Baked Pumpkin with Ginger
Baked Courgette Omelette
Braised Red Pepper and Leeks
Broccoli and Sweet Pepper Stir-Fry
Broccoli Frittata
Foil-Steamed Spring Vegetables
Lemon and Ginger Carrots
Mashed Turnips with Carrots and Orange
Orange Sherried Sweet Potatoes
Stir-Fried Vegetables with Ginger and Garlic
Tabbouleh
Tarragon Carrots
Tomatoes Provençal
Turnips Paysanne

Sauces
Tomato and Basil Sauce
Tomato Salsa

Main Courses
Almond Chicken
Beef and Vegetable Stew
Breast of Chicken Florentine

Bulgur Wheat, Tofu and Sweet Peppers
Chinese Pork and Vegetables
Creamy Pasta with Broccoli, Cauliflower and
    Mushrooms
Deep-Dish Vegetable Pizza
Eggs Florentine
Fettuccine with Fresh Tomatoes and Basil
Ginger and Apricot Stuffed Lamb with
    Kumquats
Microwave Fillets Provençal
Microwave Tarragon Chicken with Julienne
    Vegetables
Mexican Pork Stew
Mussels Sicilian Style
Navarin of Lamb
Omelette à la Jardinière
Pot au Feu
Scallops and Prawns in Wine Bouillon with
    Julienne Vegetables
Sole Florentine
Souvlakia of Lamb
Tex-Mex Chilli
Tomato Sauce Provençal with Veal on Pasta
Tuscan White Kidney Bean and Tomato
    Casserole
Winter Vegetable Stew

Desserts
Apricot Clafouti
Cantaloupe, Pear and Grapes with Sherry
    Orange Sauce
Deep-Dish Plum Pie
Melon with Blackberries
Old-Fashioned Peach Cobbler
Peach Blackcurrant Crisp
Peaches with Raspberry and Yogurt Sauce

Dishes Containing an Excellent Source of Fibre

(Over 4 g of fibre per serving)

Breakfast Dishes
Blender Breakfast
Breakfast Bran-and-Fruit Mix
Melon with Raspberries
Swiss Fruit Muesli

Lunch*
Chicken and Leek Chowder
Eggs Florentine
Potage Vert
Summer Garden Italian Soup with Pesto
Tomato and Bean Chowder
Tri-Colour Bean Soup

Salads*
Bermuda Bean Salad
Broccoli Buffet Salad
Chick Pea Salad with Red Onion and
    Tomato
Mediterranean Lentil Salad
Melon and Bean Salad
Spinach Supper Salad
White Kidney Bean Salad

*Also suitable for dinner

Dinner
Almond Chicken
Baked Courgette Omelette
Beef and Vegetable Stew
Breast of Chicken Florentine
Broccoli Frittata
Bulgur Wheat, Tofu and Sweet Peppers
Chinese Pork and Vegetables
Cracked Wheat and Basil Pilaf
Cracked Wheat with Peas and Onions
Creamy Pasta with Broccoli, Cauliflower and
    Mushrooms
Deep-Dish Vegetable Pizza
Navarin of Lamb
Sole Florentine
Tex-Mex Chilli
Tomatoes Florentine
Tuscan White Kidney Bean and Tomato
    Casserole

Desserts
Blackberries with Orange Cream Sauce
Raisin and Oatmeal Biscuits (3)
Lemon and Fresh Blackberry Tart
Peach Blackcurrant Crisp
Peaches with Raspberry and Yogurt Sauce
Raspberry Coulis (sauce)
Raspberry Meringue Torte
Raspberry Sorbet
Strawberries with Raspberry and Rhubarb
    Sauce

Guidelines for Rating the Recipes as Sources of Nutrients

As a general guide to assessing the source of nutrients, we used the definitions below.

Nutrient	Good Source	Excellent Source
Vitamin A (mg)	1.75	3.50
Thiamin (mg)	0.25	0.45
Riboflavin (mg)	0.40	0.75
Niacin (mg)	2.50	4.50
Vitamin C (mg)	7.5	15.0
Calcium (mg)	150	300
Phosphorus (mg)	150	300
Iron (mg)	2.0	4.0
Dietary fibre (g)	2.0–3.9	4.0+

All recipes in this book were tested and analysed using semi-skimmed milk, low-fat yogurt and low-fat cottage cheese.

References

Burkitt, Dennis P. "Etiology and prevention of colorectal cancer." *Hospital Practice*, February 1984, pp. 67–77.

"Cancer and Diet." Draft report. Toronto: Canadian Cancer Society, 1985.

"Cancer Prevention Research: Summary – Nutrition." Mimeographed. National Cancer Institute, 1984.

Crawley, Helen. "Food portion sizes." MAFF HMSO 1990.

Cummings, John H., and Stephen, Alison M. "The role of dietary fibre in the human colon." *CMA Journal* 123:1109–14.

"Dietary reference values, a guide." HMSO 1991.

"Dietary reference values for food energy and nutrients for the United Kingdom. Report of the panel on dietary reference values of the committee on medical aspects of food policy." HMSO 1991.

Eastwood, M. A., and Passmore, R. "Nutrition: The changing scene.' *The Lancet*, 23 July 1983, pp. 202–6.

"Does fibre-rich food containing animal lignan precursors protect against both colon and breast cancer? An extension of the 'fibre hypothesis.' " Editorial. *Gastroenterology* 86: 761–4.

Doll and Peto. "The causes of cancer: quantitive estimates of avoidable risk of cancer in the United States today." 1981.

Goldsmith, G. A., Miller, O. N., and Unglaub, W. G. "Efficiency of tryptophan as a niacin precursor in man." *Journal of Nutrition* 73:173–6, 1961.

Gori, Gio Batta. "Dietary and nutritional implications in the multifactorial etiology of certain prevalent human cancers." *Cancer* 43 (1979): 2151–61.

Handler, Semour. "Dietart fibre: Can it prevent certain colonic diseases?' *Postgraduate Medicine* 73 (1983): 301–7.

Kritchevsky, David. "Fibre, steroids, and cancer." *Cancer Research* 43: 2491S–5S.

McCance and Widdowson. "The composition of foods." 5th edition RSC MAFF 1991.

McCance and Widdowson. "The composition of foods." 4th edition, 3rd supplement; "Cereals and cereal products." RSC MAFF 1988.

McCance and Widdowson. "The composition of foods." 4th edition, 4th supplement; "Milk products and eggs." RSC MAFF 1989.

McCance and Widdowson. "The composition of foods." 4th edition 5th supplement; "Vegetables, herbs and spices." RSC MAFF 1991.

Meyskens, Frank. "Vitamin A and Its Derivatives (Retinoids) in the prevention and Treatment of Cancer." Mimeographed.

Miller, A. B. "Diet, Nutrition and Cancer." Mimeographed.

National Research Council. *Executive Summary: Diet, Nutrition, and Cancer.* Washington, D.C.: National Academy Press, 1982.

Nutrition and Cancer: Cause and Prevention. American Cancer Society, 1984.

Rietz, P. Wisso, and Weber, F. "Metabolism of vitamin A and the determination of vitamin A states. "Vitamins and Hormones 32: 237–49, 1974.

Rozen, Paul, et al. "The low incidence of colorectal cancer in a 'high-risk' population: Its correlation with dietary habits." *Cancer* 48 (1981): 2692–5.

Willett, Walter, C., and MacMahon, Brian. "Diet and cancer: An overview. Part I." *The New England Journal of Medicine* 310 (8 March 1984): 633–8.

Willett, Walter C., and McMahon, Brian. "Diet and cancer: An overview. Part II." *The New England Journal of Medicine* 310 (15 March 1984): 697–703.

Williams, R. R., et al. "Cancer incidence by levels of cholesterol." *Journal of the American Medical Association* 245: 247–52.

Index